VOL **14** NER-PEA
1143–1230

FUNK & WAGNALLS **new**
ENCYCLOPEDIA
OF SCIENCE

FUNK & WAGNALLS, INC.

HOW TO USE FUNK & WAGNALLS NEW ENCYCLOPEDIA OF SCIENCE

Volumes 1 through 21 have information printed on the front covers, spine, and title pages that make it easy to find the articles you want to read.

- Volume numbers are printed in all three places in Volumes 1 through 21.
- Letter breaks — $\frac{COL}{DIA}$ — are printed in all three places in Volumes 1 through 21. The letters above the line are the first three letters of the first article title in the volume. The letters below the line are the first three letters of the last article title in the volume.
- Page breaks — $\frac{351}{438}$ — are printed on the spines and title pages of Volumes 1 through 21. They provide the page numbers of the first and last text pages in the volume.

Articles are arranged alphabetically by title in Volumes 1 through 21. Most titles are printed in **BOLD-FACE CAPITAL** letters. Some titles are printed in even larger letters.

- Some titles are not article titles, but refer you to the actual article title. Within articles you will find *See* or *See also* other article names for further information. All of these references to other articles are called cross-references.
- Most article titles are followed by a phonetic pronunciation. Use the Pronunciation Guide on page vi of Volume 1 to learn the correct pronunciation of the article title.
- At the end of most articles are two sets of initials. The first set identifies the person who wrote the article. The second set identifies the special consultant who checked the article for accuracy. All of these people are listed by their initials and full names and position on pages v and vi of Volume 1.
- ◼ This symbol at the end of an article indicates that there is a project based on the subject of the article in the Projects, Bibliography & Index volume. The project is found under its article title, and all of the project article titles are arranged alphabetically on pages 1 through 64 of the Projects, Bibliography & Index volume.

The Projects, Bibliography & Index Volume contains three sections. Each is an essential part of the encyclopedia.

- Projects based on articles in the encyclopedia are found in the first section. Each is both entertaining and educational. Each is designed for use by a student and for parental participation if desired.
- Bibliography reading lists in the second section list books under general scientific categories that are also titles of major articles. Each book listed is marked with either a YA (Young Adult) or J (Juvenile) reading level indicator. YA generally applies to readers at the junior high level or higher. J applies to readers at grade levels below junior high school.
- Index entries for all article titles plus many subjects that are not article titles are found in the third section. Instructions on using the Index are found at the start of the Index section in the Projects, Bibliography & Index volume.

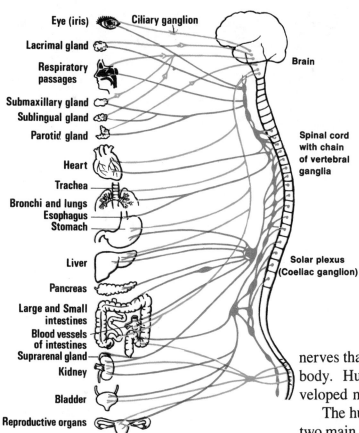

Eye (iris)
Ciliary ganglion
Lacrimal gland
Respiratory passages
Submaxillary gland
Sublingual gland
Parotid gland
Heart
Trachea
Bronchi and lungs
Esophagus
Stomach
Liver
Pancreas
Large and Small intestines
Blood vessels of intestines
Suprarenal gland
Kidney
Bladder
Reproductive organs
Brain
Spinal cord with chain of vertebral ganglia
Solar plexus (Coeliac ganglion)

The human autonomic nervous system is concerned with the control of the automatic processes of the body.

NERVOUS SYSTEM (nər′ vəs sis′ təm) The nervous system is a system for passing signals from one part of the body to another. All but the smallest and simplest of animals have special cells to do this. The cells are called neurons, or nerve cells. (*See* NERVE CELL.) Linked together, they form an internal communications network.

In the invertebrates (animals without backbones), there may be only a few nerve cells linked together. Highly developed invertebrates have knots of neurons in different parts of the body, called ganglia (plural of ganglion). At each ganglion, messages are exchanged and travel onward along different routes. In the earthworm, a ganglion at the front of the body is bigger than the others. It represents the simplest form of brain.

In the vertebrates (animals with backbones), the nervous system is more complicated. There is a brain, made of millions of neurons linked together, a spinal cord, and nerves that communicate with all parts of the body. Humans have the most highly developed nervous system of all animals.

The human nervous system is divided into two main parts. The brain and the spinal cord are the controlling parts. The brain is protected by the bones of the skull. The spinal cord is protected by the bones of the spinal column. From the brain and spinal cord, nerves extend to all parts of the body. These nerves are called the peripheral nervous system. The brain and spinal cord are called the central nervous system.

There are also two kinds of neurons. Sensory neurons carry messages from distant parts of the body toward the brain. They carry messages about temperature, pain, and pressure, and carry information from the sense organs. (*See* SENSES.) Neurons that carry messages to muscles, telling them to contract, and to glands, telling them to produce their secretions, are called motor nerves. The nerves of the central and peripheral nervous systems are a mixture of sensory and motor neurons traveling together.

Another way to divide the nervous system is by the work that different neurons do. In the voluntary nervous system, the nerves are all concerned with conscious sensations. They carry out instructions given by the brain that are directed by will. When we want to walk, or to write, or to talk, it is neurons of the voluntary system that we use. The neurons of the autonomic system are the ones that carry out routine activities that we do not normally think about. The autonomic system regulates the rate of the heart, digestion, blood pressure, and other unconscious activities.

The autonomic nervous system has divisions called the sympathetic and parasympathetic systems. Their activities balance one another. Nerve impulses in the sympathetic system tend to increase the rate of the heartbeat, and increase blood pressure. Impulses in the parasympathetic nervous system tend to have the opposite effect. Under different conditions, the different systems each take control of unconscious activities.

With training, it is possible to control some of the activities of the autonomic nervous system by will power. However, we are not born with this ability.   D.M.H.W./J.J.F.

NETTLE FAMILY The nettle (net′ əl) family (Urticaceae) is a group of plants that originated in the tropics. They have hairy, toothed leaves. The plants may grow as tall as 120 cm [4 ft].

Nettles, which have hairy, toothed leaves, usually grow in large clumps.

Nettles are known for their stinging bristles. The bristles contain formic acid, which causes a bothersome, though usually harmless, itch. A few Indonesian species of nettles may be fatal.

Some types of nettles are cooked and eaten, especially in Europe. Other types are used to make cloths and rope.

J.M.C./M.H.S.

NEUTRALIZATION (nü′ trə lə zā′ shən) The molecules of water consist of two atoms of hydrogen and one atom of oxygen. Water's formula is H_2O. A small proportion of water molecules are broken in two. These molecules are said to ionize into hydrogen ions (H^+) and hydroxide ions (OH^-). (*See* IONS AND IONIZATION.) The hydrogen ions have a positive electric charge and the hydroxide ions have a negative electric charge. Acid solutions contain more hydroxide ions than water does. Alkaline solutions, on the other hand, contain more hydroxide ions. When an alkaline solution is added to an acid solution, their hydrogen and hydroxide ions combine to form water molecules. A few of the hydrogen and hydroxide ions remain ionized. This process is called neutralization. The acid is said to be neutralized by the alkali. When the acid is exactly neutralized, the solution has the same number of hydrogen and hydroxide ions as water.

When acids and alkalis neutralize each other, they form substances called salts as well as water. (*See* SALTS.) Salts of strong acids and strong alkalies have a neutral solution. A salt of a strong acid and a weak alkali has an acidic solution. The solution is said to hydrolyze. (*See* HYDROLYSIS.) Similarly, a salt of a weak acid and a strong alkali has an alkaline solution. *See also* NEUTRAL STATE.

M.E./A.D.

NEUTRAL STATE (nü′ trəl stāt) The word neutral has different meanings in chemistry and physics, although there is some overlap between the two. In chemistry, a substance is neutral if it is neither acidic nor alkaline. Pure water is a neutral substance. Molecules of water have the formula H_2O. A small proportion of these molecules break up into hydrogen ions (H^+) and hydroxide ions (OH^-). This is called ionization. (*See* IONS AND IONIZATION.) Acid solutions contain more hydrogen ions than water. Alkaline solutions contain more hydroxide ions. When a strong acid is added to a strong alkali their hydrogen and hydroxide ions combine to form water molecules. This process is called neutralization. (*See* NEUTRALIZATION.) The acid and the alkali are said to neutralize each other.

In physics, a neutral state means an absence of electric charge. There are two kinds of electric charge: positive and negative. An object can be given either a positive or a negative charge. Suppose an object has a positive charge. Then it can be neutralized by adding a negative charge. The amount of negative charge added has to be equal to its positive charge. The object is then neutral.

M.E./A.I.

NEUTRINO (nü trē′ nō) The neutrino is one of a group of tiny subatomic particles called elementary particles. The neutrino has much less mass than an electron (probably none at all when at rest) and it always travels at the speed of light. The neutrino spins as it moves, rather like a football when it is thrown. Wolfgang Pauli was the first physicist to suggest that neutrinos existed. (*See* PAULI, WOLFGANG.) He made this suggestion in 1931 after studying a radioactive process called beta decay. (*See* RADIOACTIVITY.) All atoms contain a core called a nucleus. The nucleus usually contains particles called neutrons. (*See* NUCLEUS.) Sometimes the neutrons break up into smaller fragments. Pauli suggested that one of these fragments was a particle that had spin but no mass. This particle was named the neutrino. The neutrino was finally discovered in 1956. The neutrino is not subject to two of the four fundamental forces, so the chance of its interacting with matter is extremely small. (*See* FORCE.) A neutrino could pass through the entire planet without being stopped or deflected. Like all other elementary particles, the neutrino has an antiparticle. It is called the antineutrino. It is now known that the particle given off in beta decay is in fact the antineutrino. *See also* PARTICLE PHYSICS.

M.E./J.T.

NEUTRON (nü′ trän′) An atom is made up of a central core called a nucleus and a number of electrons. (*See* ATOM.) Most nuclei are made up of two kinds of particles, protons and neutrons. Like the proton and the electron, the neutron is a very tiny particle. It is called an elementary particle. According to current theory, the neutron is itself composed of even smaller particles, called quarks. (*See* QUARK.) Unlike the proton and the electron, the neutron has no electric charge. The mass of a neutron is slightly more than that of a proton. The neutron was discovered in 1932 by an English physicist, Sir James Chadwick.

Neutrons and protons are together called nucleons. They are called this because they make up the nucleus. For a particular element, the number of protons in the nucleus is always the same. Oxygen, for example, always has eight protons in its nucleus. On the other hand, the number of neutrons in a nucleus can vary. Atoms of the same element that have different numbers of neutrons in the nucleus are called isotopes of that element. (*See* ISOTOPE.) Most oxygen atoms have eight neutrons in each nucleus. But isotopes of oxygen exist that have nine or ten neutrons in their nuclei. Artificial isotopes can be made by firing beams of neutrons at elements. The nuclei in the atoms absorb the neutrons and become different isotopes. The extra neutrons usually make the nuclei unstable and they become radioactive. (*See* RADIOISOTOPE.)

When a neutron is outside a nucleus, it is

unstable. On average, a neutron decays in 12 minutes. This length of time is called the half-life of the neutron. Inside the nucleus, the neutrons are usually stable. When they decay inside the nucleus, the nucleus becomes radioactive. (*See* RADIOACTIVITY.) Beams of neutrons are very dangerous because they can easily penetrate through material. Scientists working in nuclear establishments have to be well protected from them. *See also* PARTICLE PHYSICS. M.E./J.T.

NEUTRON STAR (nü′ trän stär) A neutron star is an extremely small but very dense star. A neutron star is one of the final stages of a star's existence.

When a star whose mass is more than 1.4 times that of the sun exhausts its energy, it collapses and then explodes, shedding much of its mass into space. (*See* SUPERNOVAE.) If the remaining mass is no greater than that of the sun, the collapse stops, leaving a neutron star. If the remaining mass is greater, collapse will continue until a black hole forms.

A neutron star has a diameter of only a few kilometers or miles. Neutron stars are extremely dense. (*See* DENSITY.) Some astronomers think that pulsars are rotating neutron stars. (*See* PULSARS.) Others think that neutron stars are the remnants of a supernova explosion. *See also* NEUTRON; STAR; SUPERNOVA. J.M.C./C.R.

NEWT (nüt) A newt is a small salamander that belongs to the family Salamandridae. There are many different species of newts. They are widely distributed throughout the temperate regions of the Northern Hemisphere. The newts common in North America average between 5 and 10 cm [2 to 4 in] long. Newt larvae hatch from eggs in water. (*See* LARVA.) The larvae turn into another form called an eft. Efts live in moist places on land for one to three years. After this time, they change into adult newts and return to the water. Like other salamanders, newts have long, slender bodies, four short legs, and smooth, slippery skin. They eat insects, frog eggs, and worms. Very few animals eat newts. They produce a poison in their skin which not only tastes bad but can kill some animals. *See also* AMPHIBIAN; SALAMANDER. S.R.G./R.L.L.

NEWTON (nüt′ ən) The newton is the international system (SI) unit of force. (*See* FORCE; INTERNATIONAL SYSTEM.) A force of one newton gives a mass of 1 kg [2.2 lb] an acceleration of 1 m per second per second [3.3 ft per second per second]. The acceleration due to gravity is about 10 m per second per second [33 ft per second per second]. Therefore one newton is about equal to the pull of gravity on a weight of 100 gm [3.5 oz]. This is the weight of an average apple. The newton is named after the great scientist Sir Isaac Newton. (*See* NEWTON, SIR ISAAC.) M.E./R.W.L.

NEWTON, SIR ISAAC (1642-1727) Sir Isaac Newton (nüt′ ən) was an English scientist and mathematician. He was one of the greatest scientists and mathematicians of all time. He made discoveries in mathematics, mechanics, astronomy, and optics.

His most famous discovery in mathematics was calculus. (*See* CALCULUS.) Calculus is a very useful technique for mathematicians and scientists. It can be used to solve a wide range of problems.

In astronomy, Newton discovered the law of universal gravitation. This law states that every body in the universe attracts every other body. The force of the attraction depends on their masses and on the distance between them. The force that keeps the planets in their orbits is gravity. Gravity also is the force that causes a body to fall to the ground. Newton was the first to realize that gravity is the same on the earth as it is in the rest of the universe. That is why he called his theory universal. With it he calculated the shape of the orbits of the planets. He proved that the orbits were not quite circular. They were ellipses. (*See* EL-LIPSE.) Other scientists had realized that this was true. But Newton was the first to prove it mathematically, on the basis of universal gravitation. (*See* GRAVITY.)

Newton also made great contributions to the science of mechanics. His laws and theories of mechanics were published in 1687 in a book called *Philosophiae Naturalis Principia Mathematica*. This is a famous book and is now usually called just the *Principia*. It included his three laws of motion. These laws describe how forces affect the motion of a body. (*See* DYNAMICS.)

In optics, Newton experimented with prisms. He used a prism to split white light into its various colors. He was the first to suggest that white light is a mixture of different colors. He also built the first reflecting telescope. (*See* TELESCOPE.) His work on light and color was published in 1704 in a book called *Opticks*.

Newton's theories on mechanics and gravity lasted for over 200 years. It was only

Sir Isaac Newton, an Englishman who lived in the 1600s and early 1700s, was one of the greatest scientists and mathematicians of all time.

in this century that Albert Einstein proved that they were not quite accurate. He did this in his theory of relativity. (*See* RELATIVITY.) However, Newton's theories are still accurate enough for most purposes. They are widely used today by scientists and engineers.

M.E./D.G.F.

NEWTON'S RINGS (nüt′ ənz ringz) Suppose that a lens is placed on a flat mirror. The lens has one side flat and the other side is curved in a convex (outward-curving) shape. The lens rests on its curved side. If light shines down onto the mirror, rings are seen in the lens. These rings are called Newton's rings; Sir Isaac Newton scientifically observed them. (*See* NEWTON, SIR ISAAC.) When a beam of light passes through a lens, some of it is reflected (bounced off) from the bottom surface. The rest passes through and is reflected off the mirror. The beam reflected off the mirror passes back through the lens. As it passes into the lens, it combines with other beams being reflected off the surface of the bottom lens. But the beam reflected from the mirror has traveled a greater distance than the one reflected off the bottom of the lens. They may be out of step with each other. Light moves like waves, with definite wavelength. Wavelength is the distance from the crest of one wave to the next. (*See* FREQUENCY.) If the distance between the two beams of light is a whole number of wavelengths, then their crests will coincide (come together). Then the two beams reinforce each other (make each other stronger). This only happens at certain distances from the center of the lens. When this happens, a bright ring is seen. If the distance between the two beams is half a wavelength (or 1½, 2½, and so on), then they cancel out each other. This is called interference, and it produces a dark ring. (*See* INTERFERENCE.)

Newton's rings are best seen if light of one color is used. White light is a mixture of different colors. It produces rings of different

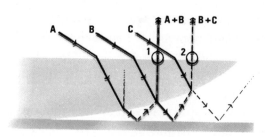

Light rays (A, B, C), reflected from the bottom of a lens and from a mirror beneath, combine to form Newton's rings. Part of A, reflected from the mirror, combines with part of B, reflected from the bottom of the lens. A dark ring (A + B) is formed (inset 1, below) because the combined rays are out of phase. Part of B, reflected by the mirror, combines with part of C, reflected from the bottom of the lens. A bright ring (B + C) is formed (inset 2, below) because the rays are in phase.

Newton's rings are best seen if monochromatic light (light of one color) is used. In the above experiment, yellow monochromatic light from a discharge lamp shines through a hole in a screen. It forms a beam which is reflected onto a convex lens resting on a mirror.

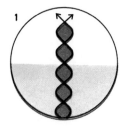

colors. For example, at certain distances from the center of the lens, the red light may cancel out. This causes a blue ring to be seen. At other distances, rings of different colors are formed. M.E./A.I.

NICKEL (nik' əl) Nickel (Ni) is a hard silvery white metallic element. Its atomic number is 28 and its atomic weight is 58.71. It melts at 1453°C [2647°F] and boils at 2732°C [4950°F]. Its relative density is 8.9.

Nickel was discovered by a Swedish chemist Axel Cronstedt in 1751. It occurs as compounds of sulfur and arsenic in minerals such as kupfernickel (niccolite). The most important ore of nickel is pentlandite, a mixture of nickel and iron sulfides. To obtain nickel the ore is first roasted. This changes the nickel compounds into nickel oxide. The oxide is then reacted with hydrogen to produce the metal. Nickel obtained in this way is not very pure. It is purified by a process called the Mond process. In this process the nickel is treated with the gas carbon monoxide. This forms a compound called nickel carbonyl. The nickel carbonyl is then heated and it decomposes into pure nickel.

Most nickel is used to make alloys. (*See* ALLOY.) Nickel alloys have many different uses. Cupronickel is an alloy of copper and nickel. It is used to make coins. Nickel silver is an alloy of nickel, copper, and zinc. It is used for making cultery. Invar is an alloy of iron and nickel. It expands very little with heat and so is used to make rulers and mechanisms in clocks. (*See* CUPRONICKEL; NICKEL SILVER.) Other nickel copper alloys are used to prepare the tubing in desalination plants for converting seawater into fresh water.

Many compounds of nickel are green. For this reason, nickel compounds are used for coloring glass. Compounds of nickel are used mainly in a process called electroplating. (*See*

ELECTROPLATING.) In electroplating an article is coated with a very thin layer of nickel to provide a protective coating.   M.E./J.R.W.

Most nickel is used to make alloys. Cupronickel is shown above. An alloy of copper and nickel, it is used in sheet-metal work, and to make coins, tableware, and tubing.

A nickel refinery is shown above. The most important nickel ore is pentlandite. The crushed ore is roasted and smelted to produce nickel oxide and then reduced to produce impure nickel. The pure metal may be refined by various processes.

NICKEL SILVER (nik′ əl sil′ vər) Nickel silver is a silvery white alloy. (*See* ALLOY.) It contains the metals copper, nickel, and zinc. It is also known as German nickel. Nickel silver is widely used for cutlery. It has an attractive color, is easy to shape, and resists corrosion. Cutlery made from nickel silver is often coated with a very thin layer of silver. Such cutlery has the letters "EPNS" stamped on it. This stands for electroplated nickel silver. (*See* ELECTROPLATING.) The amount of nickel in nickel silver varies form 5 to 35 percent. The amount of copper is between 50 and 80 percent. The rest is zinc. The more nickel the metal contains, the whiter it is. Nickel silver with about 20 percent nickel is very springy. It is used for spring contacts in telephone equipment.   M.E./A.D.

NICTATING MEMBRANE (nik′ tə tāt′ ing mem′ brān′) The nictitating membrane is a semi-transparent fold of skin that can be pulled across the eyeball. Birds and many reptiles and mammals have a nictitating membrane. Human beings do not have it, except for a very small fold at the inner corner of the eye. Where it occurs, the nictitating membrane helps to protect the eye.

J.J.A./R.L.L.

NIGHTHAWK (nīt′ hȯk′) The nighthawk is a bird that belongs to the family Caprimulgidae. It is about 22.5 cm [9 in] long with wings 55 cm [22 in] long. The nighthawk is mostly brown with white patches on its wings and tail. It flies at night, catching insects. There are two species of nighthawks in North America. The common nighthawk is found throughout North America, even in large cities. The lesser nighthawk lives only in southwestern North America. *See also* NOCTURNAL HABIT.   S.R.G./L.L.S.

A common nighthawk is pictured above. This bird is found throughout North America. It flies at night and feeds on insects.

Above, the black nightshade (*Solanum nigrum*), a common weed, has white flowers and black, poisonous berries when full grown.

NIGHTSHADE FAMILY The nightshade (nīt′ shād′) family includes about 2,000 species of herbaceous plants, shrubs, and tropical trees. They are dicotyledons and have alternate leaves. The flowers are trumpet-shaped due to the partial fusion of the five petals and the five sepals. The fruit is a berry.

Some members of the nightshade family, such as the eggplant, potato, and tomato, are popular foods. Many members of the family contain alkaloids, some of which are poisonous. (*See* ALKALOID.) The belladonna plant (*Atropa belladonna*) is also called deadly nightshade because, if eaten, the plant can cause convulsions and death. It contains the drug belladonna which, in small amounts, is a useful medicine. The nightshade plant (*Solanum dulcamara*) is also poisonous. Tobacco (*Nicotiana tabacum*) contains the alkaloid nicotine. This family also includes the mandrake (*Mandragora officinarum*).

A.J.C./M.H.S.

NIOBIUM (nī ō′ bē əm) Niobium (Nb) is a soft, silvery white metallic element. Its atomic number is 41 and its atomic weight is 92.906. It melts at 2468°C [4474°F] and boils at 4742°C [8568°F]. Its relative density is 8.6.

Niobium was discovered in 1801 by the British chemist Sir Charles Hatchett. It is obtained from ores of the metal tantalum, such as columbite and tantalite. It is added to steel to improve its strength at high temperatures. Niobium is also known as columbium.

M.E./J.R.W.

NITRATE (nī′ trāt′) Nitrates are salts of nitric acid. The formula for nitric acid is HNO_3. Nitrates are made by replacing the hydrogen (H) in nitric acid by a metal. For example, potassium nitrate replaces the H with a K (potassium). Its formula is KNO_3.

Above, Chile saltpeter (sodium nitrate) ore is blasted free from its deposits. Then it is loaded into railway cars and taken away to be crushed into small grains.

Above, after the nitrate is crushed, it is dissolved out of the crushed ore. Then it crystallizes (forms crystals) in large tanks such as the one pictured above.

Above, mechanical shovels remove the nitrate.

Purified nitrate pours from the granulation plant.

The hydrogen can also be replaced by the ammonium group to form ammonium nitrate, NH_4NO_3. All nitrates contain the nitrate ion, NO_3^-. Nitrates can be made by reacting nitric acid with either the metal, its oxide, hydroxide, or carbonate. Potassium, sodium, and calcium nitrates are important fertilizers. They supply plants with nitrogen. Many explosives contain nitrates. For example, potassium nitrate is used in gunpowder. Nitrates are used because they provide the explosive with oxygen. *See also* SALTS. M.E./A.D.

NITRIC ACID (nī′ trik as′ əd) Nitric acid (HNO_3) is a colorless liquid. It is very poisonous and corrosive, and it gives off fumes. Nitric acid dissolves most metals to form salts called nitrates. (*See* NITRATE.) Most nitric acid is used as nitrates for fertilizers. Nitric acid reacts with many organic compounds to form nitro-compounds. Some nitro-compounds, such as nitroglycerin and TNT (trinitrotoluene), are explosives. Nitro-compounds are also used in making dyes. Nitric acid is also used to make many other chemicals.

Most nitric acid is made from the gas ammonia. Ammonia and air are heated with a catalyst. (*See* CATALYST.) The catalyst is a gauze made of an alloy of platinum and iridium. The ammonia and the oxygen in the air react together to form nitric acid. The catalyst begins the reaction and helps it to go faster.

A little nitric acid is formed in the air during thunderstorms. Lightning causes the oxygen and the nitrogen in the air to combine. They form oxides of nitrogen. The oxides dissolve in the rain to form nitric acid. However, the nitric acid is very much diluted by the rainwater. M.E./A.D.

NITROGEN (nī′ trə jən) Nitrogen (N) is a colorless and odorless gas. Its atomic number is 7 and its atomic weight is 14.0067. Nitrogen boils at −195.8°C [−320.4°F] and freezes at −210.0°C [−346.0°F].

Nitrogen was discovered by the British chemist Daniel Rutherford in 1772. He was the first to publish his observations about the element. Chemists in England (Joseph Priestley and Henry Cavendish) and Sweden (Carl Wilhelm Scheele) also discovered nitrogen. A Frenchman, Antoine Lavoisier, first recognized it as an element.

Nitrogen is the most common gas in the air — 78 percent of the atmosphere. Air contains four main gases: nitrogen, oxygen, carbon dioxide, and argon. Nitrogen is obtained by cooling air until it liquefies (turns into a liquid). The carbon dioxide liquefies first and is removed. The liquid air is then allowed to boil. The nitrogen boils off before the oxygen and the argon, and so the gases are separated. This process is called fractional distillation. (*See* DISTILLATION.) Most nitrogen is used for making the gas ammonia. (*See* AMMONIA.) Liquid nitrogen is used for cooling.

Nitrogen forms many different kinds of compounds. Compounds of nitrogen with one other element are called either nitrides or azides. Nitrides are very hard substances. Many azides are explosives. Ammonia is a compound of nitrogen and hydrogen. Compounds containing ammonia are used as fertilizers. Other important inorganic compounds of nitrogen are nitric acid and nitrates. (*See* NITRATE; NITRIC ACID.) Nitrates are salts of nitric acid. Nitrogen combines with oxygen to form a number of oxides. These include nitrous oxide or laughing gas (N_2O). (*See* NITROUS OXIDE.) Nitrous oxide is a colorless gas that is used as an anesthetic. Nitric oxide (NO) is a colorless gas. It combines immediately with oxygen to form either nitrogen dioxide (NO_2) or nitrogen tetroxide (N_2O_4). Nitrogen tetroxide is a brown gas. Many organic compounds contain nitrogen. The most important of these are the amines and the amino acids. (*See* AMINE; AMINO ACID.)

Nitrogen is an essential element for life and all living things contain nitrogen compounds. Some bacteria can obtain their nitrogen from the air and convert it into nitrogen compounds. This process is called nitrogen fixation. (*See* NITROGEN FIXATION.) These nitrogen compounds are then used by plants as a source of nitrogen. These plants are in turn eaten by animals and people. Eventually the nitrogen compounds return to the soil. They are then absorbed again by plants. Alternatively they are broken down and the nitrogen is released into the air. This is called the nitrogen cycle. (*See* NITROGEN CYCLE.)

M.E./J.R.W.

NITROGEN CYCLE (nī′ trə jən sī′ kəl)

The nitrogen cycle is the continuous circulation of nitrogen among the soil, water, air, and living organisms. All living things need nitrogen. It is part of proteins and nucleic acids, both of which are vital to life. Although almost 80% of the air is nitrogen, most plants and animals cannot use nitrogen in its gaseous form. The nitrogen must be fixed, that is, combined with other elements to form usable nitrogenous compounds.

Nitrogenous compounds are formed in several ways. Some nitrogen is removed from the air by certain bacteria and algae in a process called nitrogen fixation. (*See* NITROGEN FIXATION.) Some is removed from the air by lightning. The sudden burst of electricity causes some of the nitrogen and oxygen in the air to combine, forming nitrogen oxides. When these nitrogen oxides are dissolved in water, they can combine with other elements to form usable nitrogenous compounds.

Decaying plants and animals and decaying animal wastes release ammonia, a nitrogen-containing compound. (*See* AMMONIA.) Special nitrifying bacteria convert ammonia into nitrogenous compounds that can be used by plants. Animals get their nitrogenous compounds by eating plants or other animals that eat plants. This is all part of the food chain. (*See* FOOD CHAIN.)

Although a certain amount of nitrogen is constantly being removed from the air, an approximately equal amount is being returned. Denitrifying bacteria change some of the nitrogenous compounds in the soil back into gaseous forms of nitrogen. These gases then return to the air.

Thus, in the nitrogen cycle, nitrogen starts in the air, goes through the food chain, and returns to the air. Part of this nitrogen recycles through the food chain several times before returning to the air. The complete nitrogen cycle may take a good number of years to complete. *See also* FERTILIZER; NITROGEN.

A.J.C./R.J.B.

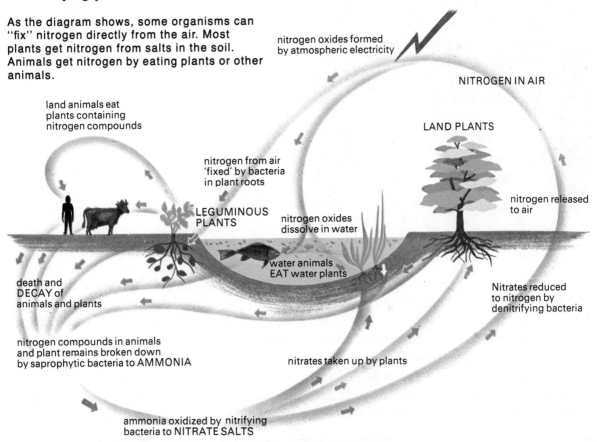

As the diagram shows, some organisms can "fix" nitrogen directly from the air. Most plants get nitrogen from salts in the soil. Animals get nitrogen by eating plants or other animals.

nitrogen oxides formed by atmospheric electricity

NITROGEN IN AIR

LAND PLANTS

land animals eat plants containing nitrogen compounds

nitrogen from air 'fixed' by bacteria in plant roots

LEGUMINOUS PLANTS

nitrogen oxides dissolve in water

nitrogen released to air

water animals EAT water plants

death and DECAY of animals and plants

Nitrates reduced to nitrogen by denitrifying bacteria

nitrogen compounds in animals and plant remains broken down by saprophytic bacteria to AMMONIA

nitrates taken up by plants

ammonia oxidized by nitrifying bacteria to NITRATE SALTS

NITROGEN FIXATION (nī′ trə jən fik sā′ shən) Plants can take simple substances like water and carbon dioxide and turn them into sugar. But they cannot make proteins with the nitrogen in the air. Plants need to have the nitrogen in the form of compounds like nitrates. They get nitrates from the soil through their roots. Some nitrates in the soil are made by bacteria from decaying animals and plants. Other nitrates are made by bacteria that can capture nitrogen from the air. The process of making nitrogen compounds from nitrogen gas is called nitrogen fixation.

Three kinds of bacteria that live in the soil and fix nitrogen are called *Azotobacter, Bacil-*

Red clover enriches the soil with nitrogen salts for other crops.

lus, Clostridium. But some bacteria, called *Rhizobium*, live inside plant roots. The roots of plants of the pea family have small knobs called nodules. Inside the nodules there are bacteria that fix nitrogen, which is helpful for the plant. The bacteria get food from the plant at the same time. This kind of living-together relationship is called symbiosis. Some other plants, like rice, have symbiotic blue-green algae which also fix nitrogen. *See also* ALGAE; BACTERIA; NITROGEN; PEA FAMILY; SYMBIOSIS. C.M./C.R.N.

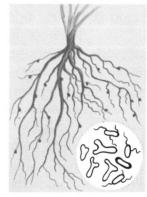

Bacteria which "fix" atmospheric nitrogen include the rhizobia, which live in nodules on the roots, right, of leguminous plants of the pea family. Rhizobia (inset right) get food from their host plants and make nitrogen salts for them.

NITROUS OXIDE (nī′ trəs äk′ sīd′) Nitrous oxide (N_2O) is also called laughing gas. It is a colorless gas that has a sweet smell and taste. People do not really laugh when they take nitrous oxide. But the gas causes them to feel no pain. If a person breathes in enough laughing gas, he or she may lose consciousness. This does not last long.

Nitrous oxide is a weak anesthetic, or painkiller. Much of it must be used if it is to work right. As a rule it is mixed with pure oxygen. Dentists use nitrous oxide as a general anesthetic and doctors use it for operations. It is useful for such purposes because nitrous oxide acts quickly and the patient quickly gets over it. J.J.A./A.D.

NOBEL, ALFRED (1833–1896) Alfred Nobel (nō bel′) was a Swedish inventor. His most famous invention is dynamite. Nobel's father was also an inventor. He was very interested in explosives, particularly nitroglycerin. Alfred Nobel started to manufacture nitroglycerin. However, nitroglycerin is a dangerous explosive because it is very sensitive to shocks. Many accidents occurred with nitroglycerin. In 1866 Nobel found that some nitroglycerin had leaked from its cask. The cask was packed in a substance called kieselguhr. Kieselguhr is an absorbent earthlike substance. He found that nitroglycerin was much safer to handle in this state. If it was absorbed into kieselguhr, it would not explode from shocks. Nobel called his discovery dynamite. He made his fortune from selling it. With his money he started the Nobel Prizes. These prizes are awarded for outstanding work in science and literature, and for promoting peace. (*See* NOBEL PRIZE.)

M.E./D.G.F.

NOBELIUM (nō bel′ ē əm) Nobelium (No) is a radioactive metallic element. Its atomic number is 102. Nobelium does not occur naturally. It was first made in 1958 by a team of American scientists. They made it by bombarding the metal curium with carbon nuclei. Seven isotopes of nobelium have so far been discovered. (*See* ISOTOPE.) The longest-lasting isotope is nobelium–255. Half of it decays in three minutes. So far only very small amounts of nobelium have been made. No uses have yet been found for the metal. Its melting and boiling points have not yet been measured. *See also* RADIOACTIVITY; TRANS-URANIC ELEMENT.

M.E./J.R.W.

NOBEL PRIZE WINNERS IN SCIENCE
Nobel prizes (nō bel′ prī′ zəs) in science are awarded each year in three fields—physics, chemistry, and medicine and physiology. Each winner receives a cash award. This award is an equal share of the year's interest from the $9 million fund set up in the will of the Swedish inventor Alfred Nobel. The Royal Academy of Science in Stockholm, Sweden, awards the physics and chemistry prizes. The medicine and physiology prize is awarded by the Caroline Institute in Stockholm. Since the prizes were first awarded in 1901, their value has varied from about $28,000 to $53,000. Quite often, prizes have been divided between two or more winners. (*See* NOBEL, ALFRED.)

J.J.A./R.W.L.

NOBLE GAS (nō′ bəl gas) The noble gases are a group of gaseous elements. The group is made up of helium, neon, argon, krypton, xenon, and radon. They are all colorless and odorless. Until the early 1960s chemists thought that they did not form any compounds at all. Then compounds of xenon, krypton, and radon with fluorine were discovered. The noble gases are also called the inert gases or the rare gases. The word inert means that they do not form any compounds at all. But they are not completely inert. Also they are not particularly rare. Therefore they are best called the noble gases.

The noble gases are all found in the atmosphere. All of them except helium and radon are obtained from the atmosphere. Helium is obtained from certain natural gas wells. Radon is obtained from the radioactive metal radium. (*See* RADIUM.) Radon is a radioactive gas and is given off when radium decays.

The existence of the noble gases was first noticed by the English chemist, Henry Cavendish, in 1785. He removed all the oxygen, nitrogen, and carbon dioxide from a sample of air. He found that he was left with a small amount of very unreactive gas. Then, in 1868, helium was discovered in the sun. (*See* HELIUM.) It was first found on earth in 1895. The other noble gases were also discovered around the same time.

M.E./J.R.W.

NOBLE METAL (nō′ bəl met′ əl) The noble metals are a group of metallic elements. The group is made up of the metals gold, silver, platinum, iridium, rhodium, osmium, ruthenium, and palladium. They are called noble because they are very unreactive. This means that they do not easily form compounds. All these metals are found by themselves in nature. Most other metals are found only combined with other elements in compounds. The noble metals are all very expensive and some of them are used in jewelry.

M.E./A.D.

Since bats are active during the night, they are said to have nocturnal habits.

NOCTURNAL HABIT (näk tərn′ əl hab′ ət) Many animals rest during the day and become active at night. These animals are said to be nocturnal. They have nocturnal habits. Diurnal animals are active during the day and rest at night. Some nocturnal animals look and act much like diurnal relatives. Others have special adaptations to help with nocturnal life. (*See* ADAPTATION.) Owls, for example, have large eyes that can see in almost total darkness. Bats "see" in the dark by sending out high-pitched sounds. Special receptors in the ears and wingtips receive an echo when the bat approaches an object.

The reasons for an animal's being nocturnal vary from species to species. Many animals are unable to tolerate the high temperatures and bright sunshine of day. For some, it is easier to find food at night. Some nocturnal animals are able to move about more freely because they do not have to worry about diurnal predators. Nocturnal habits seem to be inborn, almost like an instinct.

Many plants also have nocturnal habits. They are also called night-blooming plants. Many nocturnal plants belong to the honeysuckle and nightshade families. By blooming at night, a flower can avoid extremes of temperature and light and can be pollinated by nocturnal insects such as the moth. These flowers are usually highly scented to help the insect find it in the darkness.   A.J.C./R.J.B.

NODE (nōd) Node is a word which basically means a knot, knob, or swelling. In science, the term "node" has several different meanings or applications. In anatomy, a node is a knotty swelling, such as a buildup of lymphatic tissue (lymph node). In botany, a node is a stem joint from which a leaf starts to grow. In astronomy, a node is one of the two points where the orbit of a planet appears to cross the ecliptic. (The ecliptic is the sun's apparent path across the heavens.) In geometry, a node is the point where a continuous curve crosses or meets itself. In physics, a node is the point of a vibrating object (such as a guitar string) where there is least vibration. (*See* HARMONICS.)

J.J.A./R.W.L.

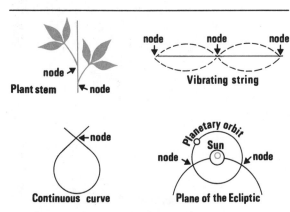

The word "node" has several applications in science, some of which are shown above.

NORMAL SOLUTION (nȯr′ məl sə lü′ shən)

A normal solution is one that contains one gram-equivalent of a substance in a liter of the solution. (*See* EQUIVALENTS.) The concept of normality is most often applied to solutions of acids and alkalis. The sum of all the atomic weights of atoms in a molecule is called the molecular weight. For example, nitric acid (HNO_3) has a molecular weight of 63. Its molecules each contain one hydrogen atom. Therefore its gram equivalent is 63 gm [2.3 oz]. Sulfuric acid (H_2SO_4) has a molecular weight of 98. But it has two hydrogen atoms in each molecule. Therefore its gram-equivalent is 98 divided by two. This is 49 gm [1.8 oz]. A normal solution of nitric acid contains 63 gm [2.3 oz] of nitric acid in a liter. A normal solution of sulfuric acid contains 49 gm [1.8 oz] of sulfuric acid in a liter. Two

normal solutions of acids contain the same amount of hydrogen. Normal solutions are used in chemical analysis. (*See* CHEMICAL ANALYSIS.) Nowadays molar solutions are usually used instead of normal solutions.

M.E./A.D.

NORTH STAR (nȯrth stär)

The North Star, or Polaris, is a bright star located one degree from the north celestial pole. (*See* CELESTIAL SPHERE.) Because of its location, the North Star is an important aid to navigators. The altitude of the North Star above the horizon is roughly equal to the observer's latitude north of the equator. The North Star is the brightest star of the constellation Ursa Minor. *See also* NAVIGATION; URSA MAJOR AND MINOR.

J.M.C./C.R.

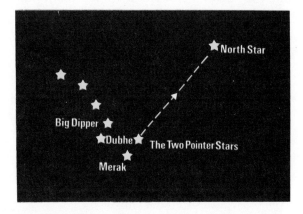

The North Star, or Polaris, always appears in the same position in the northern sky because it is almost exactly above the North Pole. It is easily located because Dubhe and Merak, two stars in the Big Dipper, point to it.

NOSE (nōz)

The nose is an organ used for smelling and breathing. When we breathe, air enters the nose through two openings called nostrils. The nostrils are separated by a thin wall of cartilage (tough tissue) and bones, called the septum. Air passes from the nostrils into two passages called the nasal passages. They lead back to the upper part of the throat. Air passes from the nasal passages through the pharynx and windpipe into the lungs.

The nasal passages have linings of soft,

mucous membrane covered with tiny, hairlike projections called cilia. The cilia wave back and forth constantly, moving dust, bacteria, and fluids from the the nose to the throat for swallowing. Large bones in the nasal passages, called turbinates, warm the air before it enters the lungs. They also stir up the air so that dust in the air sticks to the mucous membrane, and thus does not pass into the lungs.

The sense of smell is located in the highest part of the nasal cavity. The end fibers of the olfactory nerve lie in a small piece of mucous membrane about the size of a dime. These fibers carry the sensations of smell from the olfactory nerve to the olfactory lobe of the brain.

The sense of smell is closely related to the sense of taste. Some foods would not taste like they do if we could not smell them during eating. For example, we smell apples and potatoes when we eat them. But, if we were blindfolded and also had our nose blocked, we would have great difficulty in telling apples and potatoes apart by taste alone.

Colds often hamper our sense of smell. This happens because the cold infection thickens and covers the mucous membrane of the nasal passages. This prevents air from reaching the olfactory nerve. *See also* COLD, COMMON; MUCOUS MEMBRANE.

W.R.P./J.J.F.

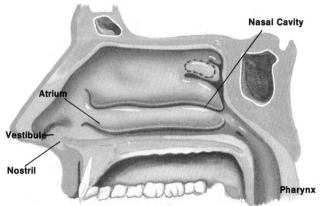

A simplified cross section of the nose and pharynx. In the nasal cavity air is warmed and moistened before traveling to the lungs.

NOTOCHORD (nōt′ ə kȯrd′) The notochord is the hard but bendable rod of cartilage (tough tissue) that extends along the bodies of all chordates. In the most advanced chordates, the vertebrates, the notochord exists only in the embryo. In adult vertebrates it is replaced by the spine, or backbone. However, in primitive chordates, such as the amphioxus, the notochord remains in the adult.

Biologists believe that the notochord's main function is to anchor the creature's body muscles so that it can swim with S-shaped movements, like a fish. With a stiff rod to pull against, this muscular action is much more efficient than it is in soft-bodied animals. *See also* CHORDATA; VERTEBRATE. W.R.P./J.J.F.

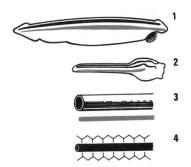

The lancelet (1) has a notochord all through its life. The seasquirt larva (2) loses its notochord at maturity. Embryos of vertebrates (3) have a notochord until the backbone forms (4).

NOVA (nō′ və) A nova is a star that suddenly increases in brightness. This happens when an explosion throws off a small amount—probably less than a hundred-thousandth—of a star's matter. This matter is a shell of gas that expands brilliantly in outer space. An exploding nova may become 100,000 times brighter than the original star. It may take a few hours or a few days for a nova to reach its maximum brilliance before it fades gradually back to its normal brightness. Astronomers are not sure exactly what causes a nova.

A recurrent nova is a nova that has had more than one observed flare-up. All novae (plural of nova) are probably recurrent. But they only flare up at long intervals. About 2 novae per year are observed in the Milky Way

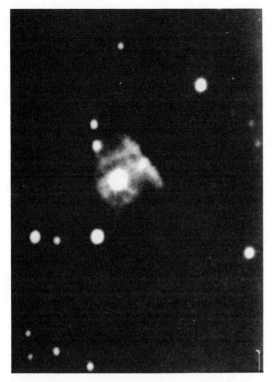
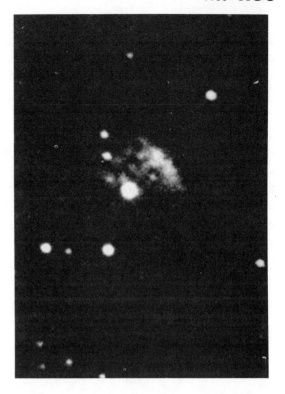

Two photographs showing the progress of a nova in the Perseus Constellation. This star flare-up was first observed in 1901. Left, the nova at its brightest in 1917. Right, the nova was much dimmer in 1933.

galaxy. Many may occur in stars too far away to be seen from earth. Other galaxies have a similar rate of nova occurrence.

A supernova is a much more spectacular event than a nova. A star may throw off one-tenth of its matter in a supernova explosion. This may result in a billion times increase in brightness. In 1054, a supernova occurred that was bright enough to be seen during the day. The remains of this explosion make up the Crab Nebula. Scientists have suggested that novae and supernovae have different origins. *See also* MAGNITUDE; STAR.

J.M.C./C.R.

NUCLEAR PHYSICS (nü′ klē ər fiz′ iks) Nuclear physics is the study of the atomic nucleus. Every atom has a nucleus at its center. The nucleus contains most of the mass of the atom. The nuclei of all elements except one contain particles called protons and neu-

trons. The one exception is the one isotope of hydrogen which has a proton only. Some nuclei, especially the larger ones, are unstable. They disintegrate and give off particles. The nucleus is then said to be radioactive. (*See* RADIOACTIVITY.) An important part of nuclear physics is the study of radioactive nuclei.

One of the most important tools of a nuclear physicist is a machine called a particle accelerator. (*See* ACCELERATOR, PARTICLE.) In these machines, beams of subatomic particles are made to collide with nuclei. This is called a scattering experiment. These collisions sometimes cause the nuclei to break up. On other occasions, the nuclei absorb the particles and turn into different nuclei. In the last 30 years, many new elements have been made in this way.

Another important branch of nuclear physics studies the structure of the nucleus. Nuclear physicists also use scattering experiments for this, though other techniques are also used. The protons and neutrons are arranged in "shells" in the nucleus. These shells have different energy levels. The protons and neutrons occupy the lowest shells that they can. These shells have the least energy. When a particle hits a nucleus, the nucleus gets energy from the particle. This sometimes causes a proton or neutron to ''jump'' into a higher shell. It then falls back into its previous shell and gives off the energy. The energy is given off in the form of a gamma ray. A gamma ray is a very energetic X ray. (*See* GAMMA RAY.) Nuclear physicists examine these gamma rays. By examining gamma rays, scientists can find out about the structure of the nucleus. *See also* NUCLEUS, ATOMIC. M.E./J.T.

NUCLEAR POWER

Nuclear power (nü′ klē ər paùr′) is one of the newest forms of energy for people. Nowadays people are using more energy than ever before. Most of this energy is supplied by fossil fuels: coal, gas, and oil. However, there is only a certain amount of these fuels in the earth. Once they are finished, new sources of energy will be needed. Many experts think that the best new source of energy is radioactive elements such as uranium. They are called nuclear fuels. Nuclear fuels are rare and expensive. However, a piece of uranium the size of a golf ball produces more energy than 1,000 metric tons [1,100 tons] of coal.

Nuclear power is obtained from the energy of the nuclei of radioactive atoms. A radioactive atom is unstable. It can be split in two. This is called fission. Fission of atoms is carried out in devices called nuclear reactors. The energy made in a nuclear reactor is changed into electrical energy. The world's first nuclear reactor was built in 1942 at the University of Chicago. It was built by a team of scientists led by the Italian physicist Enrico Fermi. (*See* FERMI, ENRICO.) Today, many countries have nuclear reactors to supply them with energy. Nuclear reactors are also used to drive ships and submarines. The United States *Nautilus* was the first nuclear-powered submarine. It was launched in 1954. The first nuclear-powered ship was the American merchant ship *N. S. Savannah*, launched in 1959. In the future, spaceships may be nuclear-powered.

Nuclear power has both advantages and disadvantages. It can make large amounts of energy and do so cheaply. However, nuclear reactors make waste that has to be disposed. This waste is radioactive. At present the waste is put into radiation-proof containers. These containers are then buried in the ground or dumped at sea. But, as more reactors are built, it will become more difficult to get rid of the waste. The fission of atoms in a reactor is controlled. The same process is used in atomic bombs, except that it is not controlled. (*See* NUCLEAR WEAPONS.) Very high standards of safety are needed in a nuclear power plant. But there is always a slight chance that a nuclear reactor might lose control. Some people argue that not too many reactors should be built. They think that other sources of energy should be used as well. These other sources include solor power and wave power. (*See* ENERGY.)

Nuclear reactions The nucleus is a small, heavy core at the center of an atom. It consists of subatomic particles called protons and neutrons. (*See* NUCLEUS, ATOMIC.) Many nuclei can be unstable and give off particles. The element is then said to be radioactive. If a large nucleus is struck by a neutron, it sometimes splits in two. This is an example of a nuclear reaction. It is called nuclear fission. (*See* FISSION.) When a nucleus splits, it gives out large amounts of energy. The nucleus can also give out neutrons when it splits. These neutrons can collide with other nuclei and split them. This is called a chain reaction. It

This is a nuclear power plant in California. Nuclear energy production has remained controversial.

occurs when there is more than a certain amount of the radioactive material. This amount is called the critical mass. If the mass is less than the critical mass, then some of the neutrons escape from the material. Therefore they do not split any nuclei and the reaction slows down. If the mass is greater than the critical mass, then not many neutrons escape. Enough neutrons collide with nuclei to keep the reaction going. If the reaction is uncontrolled, an explosion follows. If the reaction is controlled, it can be used to provide a steady supply of heat. This is what happens in a nuclear reactor.

Nuclear reactors The most important part of a nuclear reactor is called the core. The core contains the nuclear fuel. The fuel can be either a solid or a liquid. The fuel is surrounded by a coolant. The coolant is either a liquid or a gas, and often it is water. Fission of the fuel heats up the coolant. The hot coolant is pumped out of the core and into a heat exchanger. The heat exchanger contains water circulating in pipes. The coolant heats up the water in the pipes and converts it into steam. The steam is then used to drive a turbine. (*See* TURBINE.) The turbine, in turn, drives a generator to generate electricity. (*See* GENERATOR, ELECTRICAL.) In this way, heat from the fission of the fuel is converted into electricity.

Most reactors use uranium as a fuel. The uranium is a mixture of two forms called

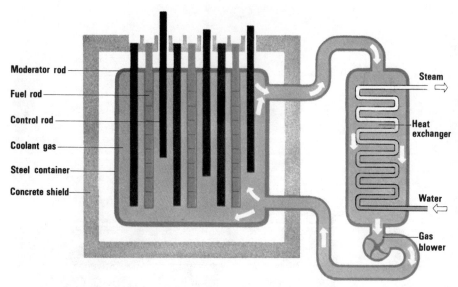

A diagram of one kind of nuclear reactor. Uranium-235 atoms in the fuel rods split apart, emitting fast neutrons. These are slowed down by graphite moderator rods. The slowed-down neutrons cause other U-235 atoms to split in a chain reaction. Control rods of neutron-absorbing cadmium regulate the rate of fission. The heat is transferred to a coolant liquid or gas. This passes to a heat exchanger to turn water into steam for generating electricity.

isotopes. All uranium atoms contain 92 protons in the nucleus. But the number of neutrons in the nucleus can vary. Atoms of the same element, but with different numbers of neutrons, are called isotopes. (*See* ISOTOPE.) The two main isotopes in uranium fuel are uranium–235 and uranium–238. They are usually shortened to U–235 and U–238. The U–235 nuclei split much more easily than the U–238 nuclei. But the amount of U–235 in natural uranium is very small and isotopes are difficult to separate. The neutrons given off by U–235 nuclei are called fast neutrons. They move at very high speeds. To start a chain reaction, they must hit a U–235 nucleus and not a U–238 nucleus. But, because of their speed, fast neutrons often escape from the fuel. Also, fast neutrons are easily absorbed by U–238 nuclei. Therefore the neutrons have to be slowed down. Slow neutrons are less likely to escape and are not absorbed by U–238 nuclei. The neutrons are slowed down by a substance called a moderator. Moderators are usually made out of graphite, water, or heavy water. (*See* HEAVY WATER.)

The chain reaction in the reactor is controlled by control rods. The control rods can absorb neutrons. They are usually made out of boron or the metals cadmium or hafnium. If the rods are lowered into the core, they slow down the reaction by absorbing neutrons. The reaction is speeded up by withdrawing the control rods.

The fission process produces dangerous radiation, as well as heat. The core is shielded with thick concrete to keep the radiation in. This protects the workers at the plant. The concrete is lined with steel as an extra safety measure.

Types of reactors The commonest type of reactor uses moderators and slow neutrons. They are called thermal reactors. Their fuel is either natural uranium or enriched uranium oxide. Enriched uranium oxide contains a greater amount of U–235 than normal uranium.

A different and important type of reactor is called the fast-breeder reactor. Its fuel is uranium oxide that is highly enriched. It is enriched either with U–235 or with plutonium–239. Plutonium–239 is an isotope of the element plutonium. It is made by bombarding U–238 with very fast neutrons. The fuel is surrounded by a "blanket" of U–238. When fission takes place, this blanket absorbs neutrons. This turns the U–238 into plutonium–239. The reaction is said to "breed" plutonium–239. The plutonium–239 that is produced can be extracted and used to enrich the fuel. The fast-breeder reactor needs no moderator. Therefore it is smaller than the thermal reactor. It uses liquid sodium as a coolant. However, there are doubts about the safety of the fast-breeder reactor. Plutonium is a very dangerous substance.

Thermonuclear power A very different kind of nuclear power is called thermonuclear power. In fission a heavy nucleus splits in two and gives off a large amount of energy. Similarly, two light nuclei can join together to form one nucleus. This is called nuclear fusion. Fusion also produces large amounts of energy. Deuterium is an isotope of hydrogen. Normal hydrogen has one proton in its nucleus. Deuterium has one proton and one neutron in its nucleus. Two deuterium nuclei can fuse together to form a nucleus of helium. Uncontrolled fusion takes place in hydrogen bombs. It is also responsible for the heat and light of the sun. To start nuclear fusion, temperatures of several million degrees celsius are needed. That is why the reaction is called thermonuclear. Scientists have not yet been able to reach these temperatures for any length of time. Another problem is controlling the reaction. If these problems could be overcome, people's energy problems might be solved. There are vast amounts of deuterium in ordinary seawater. This would supply us with an almost unlimited amount of energy.   M.E./J.T.

NUCLEAR WEAPONS (nü′ klē ər wep′ ənz) Nuclear weapons are the most deadly weapons that have ever been used. The first nuclear weapon to be built was the atomic bomb, or A-bomb. The A-bomb was first built in the United States during World War II. Two A-bombs were dropped on the Japanese cities of Hiroshima and Nagasaki. The explosive force of a nuclear weapon is measured in metric tons of TNT. The force of the bombs dropped on Japan were equivalent to 19,000 metric tons of TNT.

During the 1950s, the first hydrogen bomb, or H-bomb, was developed. The H-bomb is much more powerful than the A-bomb. Some H-bombs are equivalent to hundreds of millions of metric tons of TNT. The blast from an H-bomb can destroy an area of 500 sq km [200 sq mi]. The fire caused by an H-bomb can destroy an even greater area of about 3,000 sq km [1,000 sq mi].

How nuclear bombs work The nuclei of certain atoms can be split in two. This is called fission. (*See* FISSION.) When the nucleus splits, it sometimes gives off small particles called neutrons. These neutrons can collide with other nuclei and cause them to split. In this way the reaction can sometimes spread throughout the whole of the substance. This happens when the mass of the substance is greater than a certain mass called the critical mass. If the mass is below the critical mass, the reaction dies away and the substance is safe. In an A-bomb, the substance used is usually either of the isotopes uranium–235 or plutonium–239. They are both radioactive. An A-bomb contains two pieces of the substance. On their own they are stable because their masses are less than the critical mass. If they are brought together, their total mass is now greater than the critical mass. A nuclear reaction takes place. Some of the mass of the nuclei is converted into energy. The energy appears as light and heat, and also as the explosive blast of the bomb. The nuclear reaction gives off large amounts of radioactive products. These products are scattered over a very wide area and cause great damage.

The energy in an H-bomb is produced by fusion of deuterium and tritium. (*See* FUSION.) Deuterium and tritium are isotopes of hydrogen. In fusion, the nuclei of deuterium and tritium fuse together to form one nucleus. Fusion reactions give out much more energy than fission reactions. This makes the H-bomb much more powerful than the A-bomb. The nuclei can only fuse together at

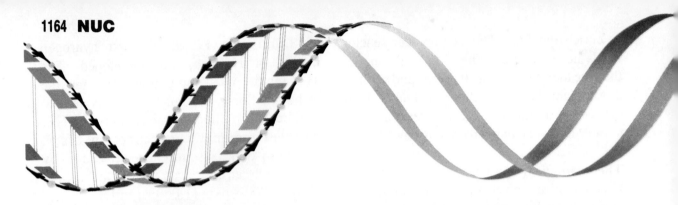

very high temperatures. Therefore large amounts of heat are needed to set the reaction going. This heat is provided by an A-bomb. Thus an H-bomb contains an A-bomb to act as a trigger.   M.E./J.T.

NUCLEIC ACID (nü klē'ik as' əd) Nucleic acids are complex chemical compounds that control the working, growth, and reproduction of all cells. A nucleic acid molecule is made of a chain of units called a nucleotide. The units of each nucleotide are phosphate, a sugar, and four nitrogen bases. In DNA (deoxyribonucleic acid), the sugar is deoxyribose and the nitrogen bases are adenine, guanine, cytosine, and thymine. In RNA (ribonucleic acid), the sugar is ribose, and the nitrogen bases are adenine, guanine, cytosine, and uracil (the uracil replaces the thymine in DNA).

DNA is composed of two nucleotide chains coiled together in a double spiral. This type of structure is called a double helix. The two chains are connected by the nitrogen bases: adenine always linking with thymine and vice versa; cytosine always linking with guanine and vice versa. Upon cell division, the DNA double helix splits so that each nucleotide chain builds a new double helix, maintaining the same nitrogen base pairs.

DNA plays a critical role in heredity. DNA and RNA control the manufacture of proteins through a process called protein synthesis. (*See* DNA; RNA.)

Protein synthesis The first step in protein synthesis occurs in the nucleus of the cell, when DNA directs the manufacture of messenger RNA (mRNA). The mRNA contains coded instructions needed to make a specific protein. The newly formed mRNA leaves the nucleus and travels to a ribosome, the site of protein synthesis. (*See* RIBOSOME.) At the ribosome, mRNA meets molecules of transfer RNA (tRNA). Each tRNA carries an amino acid. Amino acids are the "building blocks" of proteins. (*See* AMINO ACID.)

A special series of three nitrogen bases occurs on each mRNA. This series is called a codon. A similiar series, called an anticodon, occurs on tRNA. Certain codons signal the beginning of the protein synthesis process. A codon on the mRNA links with an anticodon on the amino acid-carrying tRNA. The amino acid is then deposited by the tRNA. Another tRNA links up to the mRNA, and the original tRNA leaves the ribosome. The second tRNA then deposits its amino acid. This process continues until the instructions of the mRNA are completed. This usually happens after thousands of amino acids have been added. Then a special anticodon signals the end of the protein synthesis process. The resulting chain of amino acids is called a protein. *See also* BIOCHEMISTRY; PROTEIN.

J.M.C./C.R.N.

NUCLEUS, ATOMIC All matter is made up of tiny particles called atoms. Each atom has a core in its center. The core is called the nucleus (nü' klē əs).

Lord Ernest Rutherford, a New Zealand physicist, is usually credited with discovering the nucleus because of an experiment he

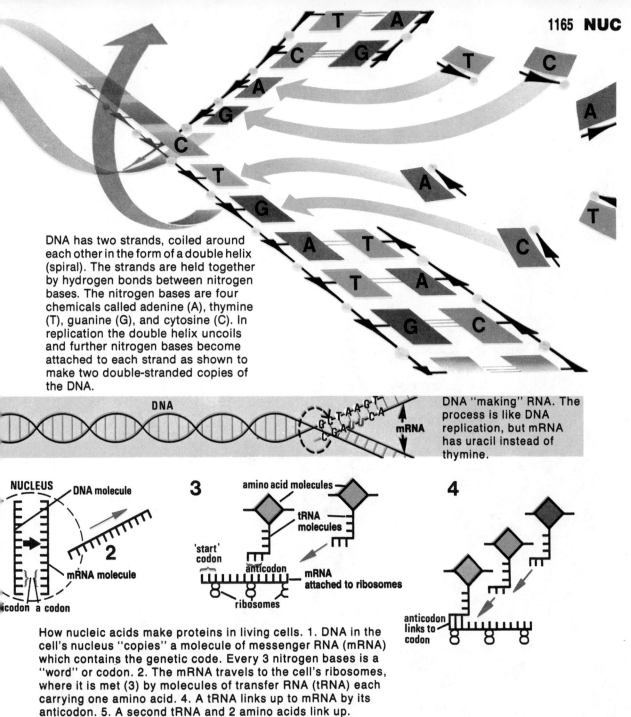

DNA has two strands, coiled around each other in the form of a double helix (spiral). The strands are held together by hydrogen bonds between nitrogen bases. The nitrogen bases are four chemicals called adenine (A), thymine (T), guanine (G), and cytosine (C). In replication the double helix uncoils and further nitrogen bases become attached to each strand as shown to make two double-stranded copies of the DNA.

DNA

mRNA

DNA "making" RNA. The process is like DNA replication, but mRNA has uracil instead of thymine.

NUCLEUS — DNA molecule

2

mRNA molecule

icodon a codon

3

amino acid molecules

tRNA molecules

'start' codon

anticodon

mRNA attached to ribosomes

ribosomes

4

anticodon links to codon

How nucleic acids make proteins in living cells. 1. DNA in the cell's nucleus "copies" a molecule of messenger RNA (mRNA) which contains the genetic code. Every 3 nitrogen bases is a "word" or codon. 2. The mRNA travels to the cell's ribosomes, where it is met (3) by molecules of transfer RNA (tRNA) each carrying one amino acid. 4. A tRNA links up to mRNA by its anticodon. 5. A second tRNA and 2 amino acids link up. 6. This happens many times until a long amino acids chain is linked to form a protein.

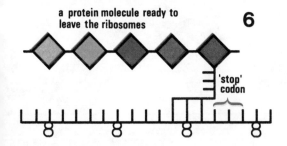

a protein molecule ready to leave the ribosomes

6

'stop' codon

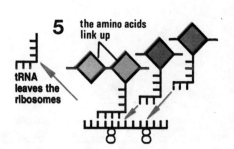

5

the amino acids link up

tRNA leaves the ribosomes

Ernest Rutherford deduced that atoms have positively charged nuclei from the fact that gold atoms (below) deflected alpha particles "fired" at them. An alpha particle has a positive electric charge, so there had to be a similar charge at the center of the atom to repel the alpha particle. Right, the nuclei of elements differ from each other because they contain different numbers of protons and neutrons. Elements can be changed into each other, or transmuted, if their nuclei can be made to gain or lose protons and neutrons. In 1920 Ernest Rutherford achieved the first artificial transmutation of elements when he produced oxygen nuclei by bombarding nitrogen nuclei with alpha particles, which resulted in the sequence shown here.

Alpha particle
2 protons
2 neutrons

Nitrogen – 14 nucleus
7 protons
7 neutrons

Alpha particle

Gold atom

Oxygen – 17 nucleus
8 protons
9 neutrons

1 proton

---

suggested and later explained. In the experiment, alpha particles were fired at a very thin piece of gold leaf. Alpha particles are tiny particles given off by certain radioactive substances. Most of the alpha particles went straight through the gold leaf. However, a few of them were deflected, some through very large angles. Because so many of the alpha particles had been able to go straight through the gold leaf, Rutherford concluded that most of an atom is just empty space. He also suggested that atoms must have a small, heavy core. This would explain why some of the alpha particles had been deflected. If the core had a positive charge, it would repel, or push away, alpha particles which also have a positive charge.

In 1920, Rutherford showed that the nucleus of a hydrogen atom contains just one particle. He called this particle a proton. At first, physicists thought that nuclei contain only protons. For example, oxygen nuclei are about 16 times as heavy as a proton. Therefore, physicists thought that the oxygen nuclei contained 16 protons. But the proton, like the

electron, has an electric charge. It has a positive charge. The electron has a charge of the same size, but negative. An oxygen atom contains eight electrons. If its nuclei contain 16 protons, then oxygen atoms would have an electric charge. But they do not have any charge. Therefore, the oxygen nuclei can only have eight protons. This caused James Chadwick to predict the neutron. The other eight particles in the oxygen nuclei are neutrons. They are slightly heavier than a proton and have no electric charge. Neutrons and protons are together known as nucleons.

There was another problem to be solved about the nucleus. Charges that are alike repel, or push each other away. Therefore, the protons in a nucleus should repel each other. This would make the nucleus split apart. In fact, most nuclei are very stable. Therefore, the nucleus must be held together by a very strong force. This force must be strong enough to overcome the electric force. It is called the strong nuclear force, or the strong interaction. It is hundreds of times stronger than the electric force. This force is believed to be caused by nuclear particles giving and taking particles among themselves. These particles are called pi-mesons, or pions. They

The hatches of this Polaris submarine (facing left) contain nuclear missiles.

were discovered in 1947.

A particular element always has the same number of protons in its nuclei. For example, oxygen nuclei always have eight protons. But the number of neutrons can vary. Atoms that have the same number of protons but different numbers of neutrons are called isotopes. For example, oxygen nuclei can have seven, eight, nine, or ten neutrons. Since it has eight protons, these isotopes can have 15, 16, 17, or 18 nucleons (nuclear particles) altogether. They are written as oxygen–15, oxygen–16, and so on. (*See* ISOTOPE.)

For lighter nuclei, the number of neutrons is about the same as the number of protons. For heavier nuclei, there are more neutrons than protons. For example, lead nuclei have 82 protons and, usually, 126 neutrons. This is because heavy nuclei tend to be unstable. The more neutrons a nucleus has, the further apart the protons are. This helps to make the nucleus more stable.

Certain nuclei are more stable than others. There is a series of numbers called "magic numbers." These numbers are 8, 20, 28, 52, 82, and 126. If the number of protons or the number of neutrons is a magic number, the nucleus is likely to be stable. This is because the nucleons are arranged in "shells" in the nucleus. A magic number is the number of protons or neutrons needed to fill the shells. For example, the first shell can take 8 protons or neutrons. The second shell can take 12. Therefore, the first two shells take $8 + 12 = 20$ protons or neutrons. When the shells are completely full with no nucleons left over, the nucleus is very stable. Lead – 208 has 82 protons and 126 neutrons. These are both magic numbers. Therefore, lead–208 is a very stable isotope. When radioactive elements, such as uranium, decay, they usually change into other radioactive elements. These elements then decay into other elements. The

The atomic nucleus contains immense energy, released in an atomic bomb explosion (facing left).

process continues until a stable element is reached. This is very often lead–208. (*See* RADIOACTIVE SERIES.)

A radioactive element is one that has an unstable nucleus. Its nuclei decay and give off particles. They can give off alpha particles, beta particles, or gamma rays. Beta particles are electrons. (*See* BETA PARTICLE.) Gamma rays are very energetic X rays. (*See* GAMMA RAY.) Both stable and unstable nuclei can be broken down by bombarding them with subatomic particles. This was first done by Lord Ernest Rutherford in 1920. He bombarded nitrogen–14 atoms with alpha particles. Alpha particles are the nuclei of helium atoms. They contain two protons and two neutrons. The nitrogen–14 atoms contain seven protons and seven neutrons. In Rutherford's bombardment, the nitrogen nuclei absorbed the alpha particles and gave off a proton. Therefore the nitrogen nuclei gained one proton and two neutrons each for a total of eight protons and nine neutrons. Since they now had eight protons, they were oxygen nuclei. One element had been changed into another. This process is called transmutation. Many new and completely artificial elements have been made in this way. M.E./A.I.

NUMBER (nəm′ bər) Whenever a person has an idea of how many objects there are in a group, such as how many coins he or she has in a pocket, that idea is called a number. Numbers are the basis of arithmetic. (*See* ARITHMETIC.)

A numeral is a written sign used to stand for a number. Counting means arranging numerals in a certain order. The numbers used for counting, such as 1, 2, 3, which are shown by Arabic numerals, are called "natural numbers." When two natural numbers are added or multiplied together, the result is another natural number.

Numbers can be shown by an order of points along a scale. Addition is performed by moving to the right. Example: $2 + 3 = 5$.

When a natural number is subtracted from another natural number, we move to the left. Sometimes, this gives another natural number. Example: $5 - 2 = 3$.

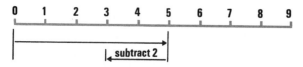

But if 5 is subtracted from 2, we come to a point on the line with no natural numbers to represent it. $2 - 5 = ?$

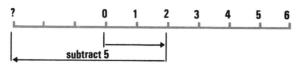

In order to subtract any two natural numbers and get a result, the system of natural numbers must be enlarged. To do this, the points left of zero are marked $-1, -2, -3$, and so on. This enlarged system is called the "system of integers." An integer is any whole number. Positive integers are $+1, +2, +3$, and so on. Negative integers are $-1, -2, -3$, and so on.

-4	-3	-2	-1	0	+1	+2	+3	+4	+5	+6

Adding a negative integer is the same as subtracting the corresponding positive integer. For example:

$$7 + (-3) = 7 - 3 = 4$$

When two integers are multiplied together, the result is an integer. For example, $2 \times 3 = 6$. However, what can 2 be multiplied by to give the answer 5? There is no answer within the set of integers. To answer this question, the spaces between the integers must be filled in by inventing some new numbers. The enlarged system is called the system of rational numbers. Rational numbers are numbers that can be written as fractions, such as ½, ¼. They include the integers in the form 2/1, −5/1, and so on. In the set of rational numbers, division by any number other than zero is possible.

Some numbers cannot be written as fractions. They are called irrational numbers. The irrational numbers include all the square roots that do not work out exactly, such as $\sqrt{2}$, $\sqrt{3}$, and so on. The number π (pi) is irrational, and so are most of the values of sines, cosines, and tangents. (*See* TRIGONOMETRY.) The rationals and irrationals together make up the system called "real numbers." In turn, real numbers are only part of a larger system that includes complex numbers. (*See* MATHEMATICAL ROOT.)   J.J.A./S.P.A.

NUMERAL (nüm′ rəl) A numeral is a written sign used to stand for a number. For example, the word "seven" or the symbol "7" is used to stand for the number of days in a week. Both "seven" and "7" are numerals. Numerals are as necessary to civilization as writing. Without numerals, there could be no mathematics and therefore no science. In ancient times, people developed systems of numerals to enable them to do the calculations needed to make calendars, measure land, and raise taxes.

The ancient Babylonians of Mesopotamia (now called Iraq) wrote cuneiform (wedge-shaped) numerals on clay tablets. Numbers from one to nine were shown as downward wedge-shaped strokes, and ten was shown by a sideways stroke. To show 20, the Babylonians wrote 2×10, to show 21, they wrote $2 \times 10 + 1$, and so on.

∇ =1 $\nabla\nabla$ =2 $\nabla\nabla\nabla$ =3 AND SO ON UP TO 9

$\triangleright$ =10 $\triangleright\nabla$ =11 $\triangleright\nabla\nabla$ =12 AND SO ON UP TO 19

$\nabla\nabla\triangleright$ =20 (2×10)

$\nabla\nabla\nabla\triangleright$ =30 (3×10)

Using this system, the number 43 is written as follows:

$$\text{VVVV} \rightharpoondown \text{VVV} = \textbf{43} \ (4 \times 10 + 3)$$

In ancient times, Egyptians used strokes for one to nine. Tens, hundreds, and so on, were shown by pictures called "hieroglyphics."

| I | 10 | 100 | 1,000 |

| 10,000 | 100,000 | 1,000,000 |

In this system, symbols were repeated to show 20, 30, and so on, rather than multiplied as in the Babylonian system. The Egyptian way of writing the number 2,435 was as follows:

$$= \textbf{2,435}$$
(1,000+1,000+100+100+100+100+10+10+10+5)

Chinese numerals are grouped in tens, but use multiplication for 20, 200, and so on. Below are examples of Chinese numerals, and an illustration of their use to write the number 1,876. The numbers are written vertically, with the units at the bottom.

1	2	3	4	5	6
一	二	三	四	五	六

7	8	9	10	100	1,000
七	八	九	十	百	千

$$\left.\begin{array}{l}千\end{array}\right\} = 1 \times 1,000$$

$$\left.\begin{array}{l}八\\百\end{array}\right\} = 8 \times 100$$

$$\left.\begin{array}{l}七\\十\end{array}\right\} = 7 \times 10$$

$$\left.\begin{array}{l}六\end{array}\right\} = 6$$

The ancient Greeks and Romans used letters of their alphabets for numerals. This made calculations quite complicated. It is surprising that the Greeks made so much progress in mathematics. The letters used by the Romans were:

I	V	X	L	C	D	M
1	5	10	50	100	500	1,000

Repetition or subtraction were used to show numbers between one, five, ten, and so on. Thus, two and three were II and III, and six, seven, and eight were VI, VII, VIII. But four and nine were written as IV and IX, that is, "one before five" and "one before ten." The Romans therefore wrote the number 2,738 as MMDCCXXXVIII.

The most important step in the development of numeral systems was the introduction of a zero symbol (0). This idea probably began in India and was borrowed by the Arabs, whose system we use today. By using one or more zeros, a single set of symbols (1 to 9) can show tens, hundreds, thousands, and so on, as well as units, by their position. This is called "place value." For example, 4,305 means four thousands, three hundreds, no tens, and five units. By using place value, the Arabic system simplifies calculations involving large numbers. *See also* ARITHMETIC; BINARY NUMBERS. J.J.A./S.P.A.

NUTHATCH (nət' hach') A nuthatch is a small bird that belongs to the family Sittidae. Its average length is 14 cm [5.5 in]. The nuthatch was named for their habit of tucking nuts into the crevices in the bark of trees to hold them in place while they peck them open. A nuthatch eats mainly insects, which it searches for by creeping up and down trees. It is the only bird that can easily climb down a tree headfirst.

There are about 25 species of nuthatches in the world. Four species are found in North America. The best-known North American species is the white-breasted nuthatch. It has a gray back and wings; a short, gray tail; a long, slender bill; a black "cap" on top of its head; and a white breast. It lives in the eastern half of North America and is commonly seen around bird feeders during the winter.

S.R.G./L.L.S.

NUTRITION (nü trish' ən) Nutrition is the science of food. It deals with the composition (chemical make-up) of foods, how food is taken in and used by plants and animals, and the effects of food on health.

Dietetics is an important branch of nutrition. Dietetics is concerned with people's food needs and the construction of a balanced diet that meets these needs. Dietitians carry out important work in hospitals, schools, and other institutions. (*See* DIET.)

Some nutritionists also develop and test new foods, such as the foods used in space exploration, foods made from algae, and foods made from chemicals.

Other nutritionists may study how living things use food. Using such methods is labelling foods with radioisotope tracers, these scientists can follow the path of a particular food through the body. In this way, the scientists try to discover what biochemical reactions of the body the food takes part in. (*See* RADIOISOTOPE.)

Even many years after the discovery of vitamins, their exact roles are not understood. For example, vitamin D (which cures and prevents rickets, a bone disease) is known to

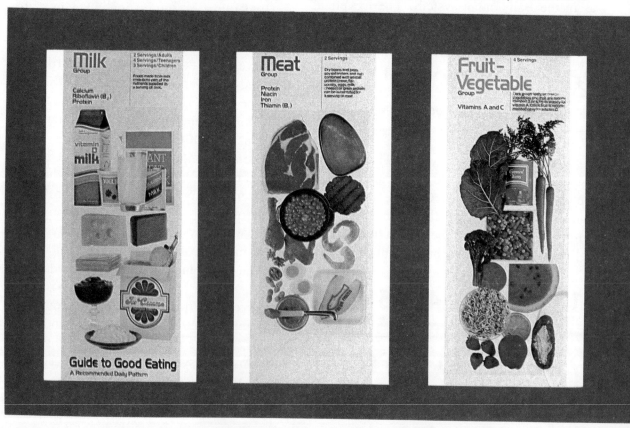

affect the absorption of calcium from the intestines. Calcium is a vital substance of bone tissue. But exactly how vitamin D performs its function is not clear.

Most animals in the wild eat a balanced diet by instinct, but nutritional research is important in making sure that those in captivity (such as zoos) receive the right foods to stay healthy.

Personal nutrition   People need certain nutrients for building and maintaining healthy bodies. They are proteins, carbohydrates, fats, minerals, and vitamins. Water is also essential.

Protein builds the body's tissue and is the basic substance of every cell. It is found in foods of animal origin, such as meat, fish, poultry, eggs, and milk. Protein is also found in some cereal grains, vegetables and fruits, and legumes (such as soybeans and chickpeas).

There are three forms of carbohydrates— starch, sugar, and cellulose or fiber. All are needed for energy and regularity. Carbohydrates also help the body to use fats.

Fats are very concentrated energy sources. They make up part of the cell structure and protect vital organs. Foods which provide fat include butter, margarine, salad oils, nuts, egg yolks, and meat, and such plants as corn, peanuts, and soybeans.

Minerals are needed by the body in small amounts. Calcium is largely responsible for the hardness of bones and teeth. Iodine, iron, magnesium, potassium, and phosphorus are among the other essential minerals.

Vitamins help release the energy from foods, promote normal growth, and keep the nerves and muscles functioning properly.

A balanced daily diet includes portions from each of four major food groups. Proper foods provide nutrients for good health.

Meat group: Two or more servings of beef, veal, lamb, poultry, eggs, fish, dry beans and peas, nuts, or peanut butter.

Vegetable/fruit group: Four or more servings of vegetables and fruits, including at

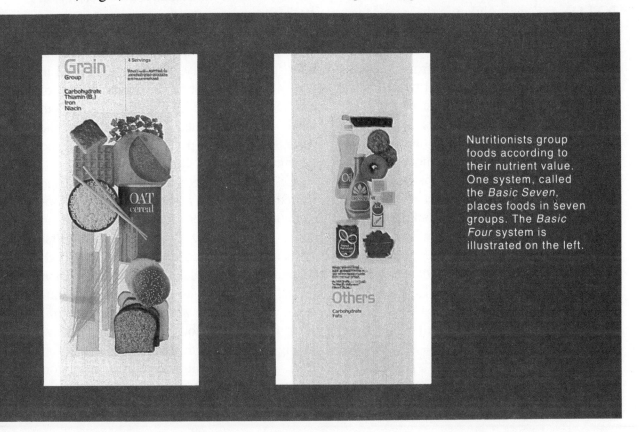

Nutritionists group foods according to their nutrient value. One system, called the *Basic Seven*, places foods in seven groups. The *Basic Four* system is illustrated on the left.

least one serving of a leafy green vegetable.

Milk group: Milk every day for everyone, especially children—three or more servings of milk, cheese, ice cream, and other dairy products.

Bread/cereal group: Four or more servings of breads and cereals, including crackers, grits, pasta (macaroni, spaghetti, noodles, etc.), and rice.

Nutritionists stress the importance of varying the choices from day to day. They also warn against "empty calorie foods," which contain a high proportion of calories to the amount of nutrients. (*See* CALORIE.)

The science of nutrition overlaps into various other fields of science. Nutrition is part of medicine, physiology, and biochemistry. Chemists make synthetic (artificial) foods from chemicals and educators teach correct food habits. Researchers in agriculture also work to develop high-yield and high-quality crops. *See also* CARBOHYDRATE; FAT; PROTEIN; MINERAL; VITAMIN.

J.J.A./J.J.F.

NYLON (nī′ län′) Nylon is the name for a family of synthetic resins known as thermoplastics. (*See* PLASTIC.) These materials are made from chemicals derived from coal, water, air, petroleum, agricultural by-products, and natural gas. Nylon is one of the most important chemical discoveries. It is one of the toughest, strongest, and most elastic substances we have. Kevlar is another. Nylon can be formed into fibers, bristles, sheets, rods, tubes, and coatings. It can also be made in powdered form for use in making molds.

Nylon fabrics resist mildew and are not harmed by most kinds of oil, grease, and household cleaning fluids. Nylon absorbs little water.

Most nylon produced in the United States is made from two chemical compounds: hexamethylenediamine and adipic acid. Hexamethylenediamine contains carbon, nitrogen and hydrogen. Adipic acid contains carbon, hydrogen, and oxygen. Manufacturers combine the two compounds to form a substance called nylon salt. A solution of nylon salt is placed in an autoclave (a heating device). The autoclave heats the solution under pressure. Water is removed, and the small molecules in the compound combine to form large molecules. This process is called polymerization. (*See* POLYMERIZATION.)

In some factories, the newly-made nylon comes out of the machines as a plastic ribbon, which is then cooled and cut into small pieces. Nylon fibers are made by forcing molten nylon through tiny holes in a device called a spinneret. The thin streams of nylon that come out of the spinneret harden into filaments when they strike the air. Then they are wound onto bobbins. From one to as many as 2,520 filaments are united into a textile nylon yarn. The fibers are drawn, or stretched, after they cool. This stretching action causes the molecules in the fibers to fall into a straight line, which makes the fibers stronger and more elastic.

Nylon was first made into hosiery in 1937. Since then, many uses have been found for it. Nylon is used to make many articles of clothing, parachutes, carpets, rope, fishing lines, and upholstery. Nylon is also used in tires and for bristles in many types of brushes. Solid pieces of nylon are used to make bearings, gears, and small machine parts. Unlike metal parts, nylon bearings and machine parts need little lubrication.

E. I. DuPont de Nemours & Co., of the United States, was a leader in the development of nylon. Experimentation with it began in the 1920s, and DuPont produced the first nylon in 1935. Called Nylon 66 because both chemicals used in making it have six carbon atoms, Nylon 66 is now produced by manufacturers around the world. There are several other forms of nylon manufactured today, among which are Nylon 6 and "Qiana." The latter, one of the more recent of the nylon derivatives, is a silklike nylon fiber used in clothing.

W.R.P./J.M.

NYMPH (nimf) Insects change in body shape and size during their lives. When a young insect hatches, it rarely resembles its parents. The insect undergoes several changes before it becomes an adult. These changes are called metamorphosis. *(See* METAMORPHOSIS.*)*

A nymph is a stage in the growth of certain groups of young insects when they do look similar to their parents. Species of insects that go through a nymphal stage do not undergo complete metamorphosis. Nymphs shed their outer skins from time to time as they grow. *(See* MOLTING.*)* Silverfish, mayflies, dragonflies, termites, grasshoppers, mantids, lice, bugs, and some other insects begin life as nymphs. *See also* LARVA.   S.R.G./J.E.R.

A nymph is a young insect which undergoes only partial metamorphosis as it becomes an adult. The mantis nymph (above) looks like an adult except that it has no wings.

The mayfly nymph (above) lives in water and does not look much like the adult.

OAK (ōk) Oaks are trees which belong to the beech family and to the genus *Quercus*. *(See* BEECH FAMILY.*)* They can grow from 18 to 33.3 m [60 to 110 ft] tall. The leaves of oaks usually have several lobes, or projections, along the edge. During autumn, the leaves of some species of oak trees turn brilliant colors. The fruit of the tree is called an acorn. An acorn is a small nut with a cap on the top of it and a seed inside. Acorns are important as a food for wildlife.

There are more than 200 species of oak trees in the world. About 58 species grow in North America. Oaks grow in temperate climates and are a valuable source of wood for building and fuel.   S.R.G./M.H.S.

Oak trees have simple, usually lobed leaves, and fruits, or acorns, which are held in cups at the base. The close-grained, tough wood was formerly much used in building ships, and makes fine panelling for walls.

OAK RIDGE NATIONAL LABORATORY The Oak Ridge (ōk rij) National Laboratory is where a great deal of nuclear technology has been developed. It is located in Oak Ridge, Tennessee, about 29 km [18 mi] from Knoxville.

The Oak Ridge National Laboratory was established during World War II. Its somewhat isolated location is convenient to power sources and transportation. Materials for atomic bombs were manufactured in Oak Ridge during the war. Oak Ridge thrived during the war, but it has now shrunk to about one-third of its peak size. Today, the Oak Ridge National Laboratory concerns itself with the peacetime applications of nuclear energy, as well as other projects. Scientists there have done much research into radioactive drugs. Other work includes the conversion of saltwater into fresh water. *See also* NUCLEAR POWER; NUCLEAR WEAPON.

J.M.C./R.W.L.

OATS (ōts) Oats are important cereal crops that can grow in poor quality soil. They are members of the genus *Avena* of the grass family, and are related to corn, barley, wheat, and rice. The oat plant reaches a height of about 1 m [3.3 ft]. It has 40 to 50 side branches, each of which ends in a flower cluster called a spikelet. Each spikelet contains two seeds which are enclosed in husks.

Oats have the highest food value of any of the cereal grains. They are rich in carbohydrates, proteins, fats, calcium, iron, and vitamin B_1. Oats are cultivated primarily as livestock feed. The seeds, once removed from the husks, can be used to make oatmeal, breakfast cereals, cakes, and cookies. The most popular variety in the United States is common oats (*Avena sativa*). *See also* CEREAL CROP; GRASS.

A.J.C./F.W.S.

OBSERVATORY (əb zər′ və tōr′ ē) An observatory is a building specifically designed for observation and study of stars, planets, meteors, and other aspects of the universe.

Study of the movements and changes in appearance of the sun, moon, stars, and planets began in ancient times, as long ago as the sixteenth century B.C. There is evidence of astronomy in ancient England, Egypt, Babylonia, China, and Central America.

The single most important advance in the development of astronomical observatories was the production of practical telescopes at the start of the seventeenth century A.D. The instruments used by astronomers up to that time included the sextant, quadrant, astro-labe, and armillary sphere. (*See* NAVIGATION.) By 1610, Galileo had made many discoveries using a single-lens-type telescope.

Observatories made use of other techniques as they developed. The spectroscope, photometer, photographic camera, digital electronic computer, and other more specialized instruments have important uses for astronomers. (*See* CAMERA; PHOTOMETRY; SPECTROSCOPE.) The history of observatories is primarily a history of the refinements of telescopes and the other instruments used for observing and studying astronomical objects.

Optical telescopes There are three types of optical telescopes. A refracting telescope uses one or more glass lenses to bring light from distant objects into focus as an optical image. A reflecting telescope uses one or more mirrors to accomplish the same goal. A third type, combining both lenses and mirrors, is called a catadioptric telescope.

The improvement of refracting (or refractor) telescopes reached a peak in the nineteenth century. Use of several glass lens-elements made a telescope's viewing power strong, but each element slightly reduced the intensity of the light passing through it. (*See* OPTICS.) The refracting telescope is limited in its ability to aid in observation of faint stars and galaxies. The most serious drawback of this type of telescope is that all colors of light cannot be brought into focus at the same time (chromatic aberration).

The reflecting telescope was developed to avoid the distortions of the refracting telescope. It uses a system of curved, surface-coated mirrors rather than lenses to collect light rays and focus them.

The largest refracting telescope is at Yerkes Observatory in Williams Bay, Wisconsin. It was built in 1897, and it has a lens 102 cm [40 in] in diameter. The largest reflecting telescope is at Special Astrophysical Observatory, near Zelenchukskaya, Russia. It was built in 1974, and it has a mirror 600

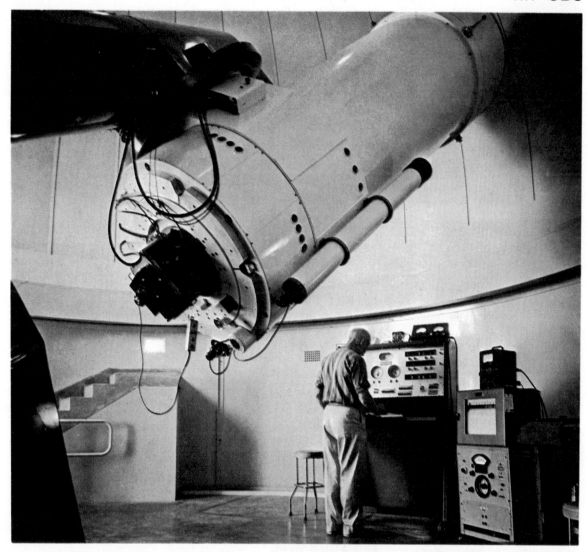

Above, the 102 cm [40 in] reflector telescope at Australia's Siding Spring Observatory is located high in a remote mountain range.

cm [236 in] in diameter. The mirror of the largest reflecting telescope in North America—at Mount Palomar Observatory, near San Diego, California—has a 508-cm [200-in] diameter. It was built in 1948. A recent innovation in telescope design is the multiple-mirror telescope. A six-mirror version with power equivalent to a 450-cm [176-in] reflector was completed in 1979 at the Whipple Observatory, near Tucson, Arizona.

Since 1900, most observatories have used reflecting rather than refracting telescopes. Catadioptric telescopes are usually designed for special purposes, such as wide-angle photography of star fields.

Optical telescopes are seldom used for

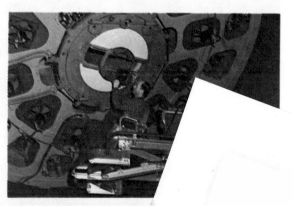

Above, the mirror cell of th
telescope at Mount Palon

direct observation. Instead, astronomers study photographs taken of the telescopic image. These photographs are often made with long-duration exposures, so that light images too dim to be seen by the human eye will register on photosensitive film. During such exposures, any vibration will result in a blurred image.

In any kind of optical telescope, therefore, the mounting is extremely important. It must not only be massive to minimize vibrations, but must provide precise movement of the telescope. The mounting must also include mechanisms able to compensate for the earth's rotation during photographic recording of the optical image. The motion of the telescope is often regulated by some type of clock-drive device and by computer.

Optical telescopes are located at high altitudes away from large cities to avoid the blurring effects of heat waves, smog, and city lights. They are often enclosed in a large, dome-shaped structure that can be rotated to point the telescope in any direction. The dome can be closed off to protect the tele-

scope from bad weather.

Radio telescopes   A radio telescope is designed to detect and record electromagnetic waves from outer space. It usually consists of a large, bowl-shaped reflector (or "dish") that acts as an antenna for radio waves. The signals detected by the antenna—which can be aimed and focused—are amplified and recorded for study. The characteristics of a signal enable astronomers to calculate the temperature and composition of the object that radiated it.

Radio telescopes can be made much larger than any optical telescope. They are used to study galaxies and other objects that are very distant or give off no visible light. Radio telescopes are usually located in valleys to minimize interference from earth's radio waves.

A radio telescope with a single reflector 305 m [1,000 ft] in diameter was put in oper-

Shown below are the domes of the Kitt Peak National Observatory near Tucson, Arizona.

ation in 1963 in Arecibo, Puerto Rico. A more powerful type of radio telescope can be constructed using two or more reflectors. This type—called a radio interferometer—produces clearer radio images than any single-reflector radio telescope could. A radio interferometer constructed at the National Radio Astronomy Observatory in Socorro, New Mexico, in 1980, combines 27 reflectors. Each reflector in this Very Large Array (VLA) telescope is 25 m [82 ft] in diameter.

Space telescopes Astronomers have helped to develop observatories that orbit the earth. The first, launched by the Soviet Union in 1968, carried eight telescopes and operated for six weeks. Later that year, the United States launched its own satellite observatory, the OAO 2, which transmitted picture of the planets back to earth. Scientists plan to have the Space Telescope (ST) satellite in orbit before 1990. The ST will have a 2.4 m [94.5-in] reflector telescope, a wide-field planetary camera, a faint-object spectrograph, a high-resolution spec-

This is a Very Large Array (VLA) radio telescope. The VLA has twenty-seven antennas, which can be arranged differently for various kinds of observation.

trograph, and a high-speed photometer.

The advantages of the ST over earth-based telescopes are many. The ability of its telescope to detect faint objects will be ten times greater because it will be free of the "smear" effect caused by the earth's atmosphere. It will be able to operate night and day. It will be able to detect ultraviolet and infrared radio waves, which are largely absorbed by the earth's atmosphere. Its photographic images will not be contaminated by the light scattered by the earth's atmosphere in the night sky.

Astronomers hope that the ST and similar space observatories will help resolve some of the many riddles of the universe. *See also* ASTRONOMY; ASTROPHYSICS; BLACK HOLE; SOLAR SYSTEM; UNIVERSE.   P.G.Z./G.D.B.

OBSIDIAN (əb sid′ ē ən) Obsidian is volcanic glass. It forms when molten (melted) lava cools too quickly for crystals to form. It is usually black or black with red streaks. The chemical composition of obsidian is the same as that of granite. Obsidian breaks easily into sharp fragments. These fragments were once used by American Indians for arrowheads. Obsidian is also used in jewelry and in various art objects. *See also* LAVA.   J.M.C./W.R.S.

OCEANOGRAPHY (ō′ shə nǎg′ rə fē)

Oceanography is the study of the oceans of the world. Although oceans cover 71 percent of the earth's surface, little is known about them. Oceanography is one of the youngest sciences.

There are five oceans: the Atlantic, Pacific, Indian, Arctic, and Antarctic. There are smaller bodies of water called seas, sounds, bays, and gulfs. All of these bodies of

salt water are connected to each other. Oceanographers study all of them.

Oceanography is divided into four branches. Physical oceanography is the study of the temperature, currents, tides, and ice formation of the oceans. Geological oceanography is the study of the coastlines, islands, and floor of the oceans. Chemical oceanography is the study of the chemicals in the seawater. Biological oceanography is the study of the plants and animals that live in the oceans. It is usually called marine biology. (*See* MARINE BIOLOGY.)

Ocean currents   The water in the oceans is not still. It is always moving in regular patterns. These patterns are made up of currents—strong movements of water in one direction. There are many kinds of currents. One kind is a "stream." A stream is a current with distinct boundaries. The Gulf Stream, off the east coast of North America, is an example of a stream. It flows from near the Gulf of Mexico north to Canada like a river in the middle of the Atlantic Ocean. A "drift" is a current that does not have distinct boundaries. The water in one area of the ocean shifts slowly in a general direction.

The world's ocean currents. 1. North Pacific Drift. 2. California Current. 3. North Equatorial Current. 4. Equatorial Countercurrent. 5. South Equatorial Current. 6. Peru Current. 7. West Wind Drift. 8. Cape Horn Current. 9. Labrador Current. 10. Gulf Stream. 11. North Atlantic Drift. 12. Canaries Current. 13. Guinea Current. 14. Brazil Current. 15. Benguela Current. 16. Agulhas Current. 17. Monsoon Drift. 18. Indian Counter Current. 19. North Equatorial Current. 20. South Equatorial Current. 21. West Australian Current. 22. Oya Shio. 23. Kuro Shio. 24. East Australian Current.

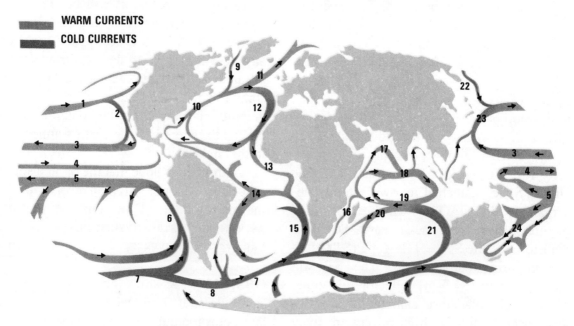

WARM CURRENTS
COLD CURRENTS

Currents are caused by several things. Winds push water into currents. The differences in water temperature and salt content cause currents, too. Cold and salty water is heavier than warm and less salty water. When cold, salty water sinks, it pushes other water up, causing currents. Currents are also caused by the rotation of the earth. The circulation of seawater in the northern hemisphere is clockwise while the circulation in the southern hemisphere is counterclockwise. (*See* CORIOLIS FORCE.)

Tides are a type of regular current, changing direction every six hours. They are caused by the gravity of the moon and sun. (*See* TIDE.)

Currents are important to the plants and animals in the oceans. The movement of water brings them food and nutrients. It also helps them during migrations. (*See* MIGRATION.) Currents also affect the climate of land. (*See* CLIMATE.) When a warm current passes near land, the weather of that land is usually warm. In the past, currents played an important role in helping sailors move from one land to another and in allowing widespread exploration on the earth.

Ocean waves   Waves are temporary movements of water for short distances. They are usually caused by winds. Some waves can be caused by something moving through the water, such as a ship, or a movement underwater, such as an earthquake. Waves usually affect only the surface water. They are rarely higher than 4 m [13.2 ft] but may reach 12 m [40 ft] in height during storms. The largest wave recorded, which was caused by an earthquake, was 34 m [112 ft] high. Waves caused by earthquakes are often called tidal waves. In some places tidal waves are referred to as tsunamis. (*See* TSUNAMI.)

Ocean bed   The bottom, or floor, of the ocean is often called the ocean bed. The ocean bed is similar to the land near the water. It has flat areas, valleys, and mountain ranges. Islands are the tops of underwater mountains which stick out of the water. Some of these mountains are volcanoes. (*See* VOLCANO.)

The ocean is shallowest near land. The ocean bed has a gradual slope called the continental shelf, where much of the sea life and valuable resources such as oil are found. At the edge of the shelf the ocean bed drops off quickly to deep areas of the ocean called the abyss. There are deep valleys or trenches at the bottom of the abyss. The Mariana Trench in the Pacific Ocean is the deepest point in the world. Here the ocean bed is 10,752 m [35,275 ft] deep—over 10 km [6 mi] deep.

Oceanic floor research   The ocean floor is one of the three main features of the earth. The other two are the continents and the Mid-Oceanic Ridge. Modern oceanography is concerned with all three. By learning about the ocean floor, oceanographers hope to find out more about the age of the earth. In so doing they can learn about the continents and test the continental drift theory. Studying the Mid-Oceanic Ridge will help them to understand ocean currents and mountain formation.

The cooperative work of scientists who took part in the International Geophysical Year of 1957-1958 set the stage for great advances in oceanography. The discovery of the Mid-Oceanic Ridge and the record-breaking dive into the Mariana Trench by the U.S. Navy's bathyscaphe *Trieste* early in 1960 was only the beginning. Oceanographic institutions all over the world quickly initiated large-scale projects to expand and apply the new knowledge. They also applied advanced technology, borrowing the best that electronics and modern engineering could offer.

A notable example was the Deep Sea Drilling Project of the National Science Foundation (NSF), in effect from 1966 to

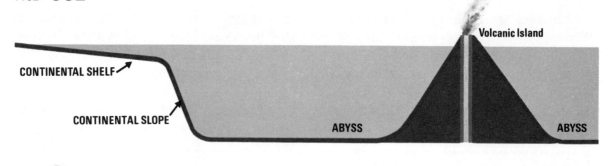

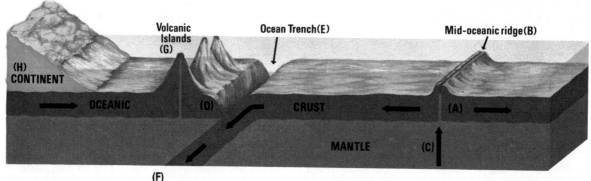

Typical ocean profile. The shallow continental shelf ends in a steep slope which plunges to the ocean deep, or abyss. Mountains and volcanoes rise from the abyss, some forming islands. Above, according to the theory of continental drift, oceanic crust (A) is made along mid-oceanic ridges (B) by molten rock welling up from the earth's mantle (C). Plates formed by the new crust collide with other plates (D) and are forced down. Where they meet, an oceanic trench (E) is formed. Friction of the descending plate (F) melts rock, which forms volcanic islands (G). Friction also causes earthquakes in the continental mass (H).

1983. This program used a converted off-shore oil rig vessel, the *Glomar Challenger,* to drill and bring up samples of sediment, called cores, from the ocean floor. These cores provided additional evidence to support the theory of continental drift. (*See* CONTINENTAL DRIFT.) In 1984, the NSF began a new project called the Ocean Drilling Program using a more advanced ship, the *JOIDES Resolution,* which made its first cruise in 1985. On board the new drilling ship is the largest, most varied array of oceanographic research equipment in the world, as well as two mainframe computers linked to 50 small computers located throughout the ship. (*See* MICROCOMPUTER.)

One of the great modern aids to ocean basin research has been the development of small submersibles. These are diving vessels that enable their occupants to get a firsthand look at the ocean bottom. One such vessel is the Woods Hole Oceanographic Institution's *Alvin. Alvin*'s exploration of the Galapagos Rift Valley startled the world. Looking for a cause of previously observed high temperatures in waters more than 2,500 m [8,000 ft]

deep, the *Alvin* crew discovered vents that poured hot water into the icey ocean from beneath its floor. From the chimney-like vents, some almost 9 m [30 ft] high, water at temperatures of up to 300°C [570°F] was pouring. Dissolved in the water were sulfide minerals of metals such as copper, nickel, and cadmium. This discovery provided geologists with new insights into how mineral deposits form.

Marine biologists then discovered that previously unknown forms of sea life were living around the vents. They found that giant shellfish and tube worms up to 3 m [9 ft] long are able to live at these depths without sunlight by obtaining the energy they need for growth and metabolism from sulfur-digesting

Progress in oceanographic research has been made possible by apparatus like the *Tektite 1* habitat (shown in the artist's simulation above). In 1969, four U.S. aquanaut scientists in *Tektite 1* spent 60 days on the sea bed near the Virgin Islands.

bacteria that thrive in the hot, sulfurous water. *See also* CONSERVATION; OXYGEN; PLANKTON.   S.R.G./R.J.B.

OCELOT (äs′ ə lät′) The ocelot (*Felis pardalis*) is a cat found in regions ranging from southern Arizona and Texas of the United States, through Central America, to Paraguay and northern Argentina in South America. The ocelot lives in forests, spending most of its life on the ground. But this cat is also an able climber. It often hunts in trees. A medium-sized member of the cat family, the ocelot is 107 to 120 cm [3.5 to 4 ft] in length, including the tail.

Ocelots are nocturnal hunters. They feed on mice, rabbits, snakes, birds, and monkeys. A black-spotted animal, the ground coat of the ocelot varies greatly in color, from reddish yellow to gray. The belly is usually white, marked with black. The animals have been hunted nearly to extinction for their fur. If caught when young, the ocelot is tamable.

                                    J.J.A./J.J.M.

OCTANE RATING (äk′ tān′ rāt′ ing) Octane rating is a way of describing the quality of gasoline. Internal-combustion engines are the engines used in automobiles, trucks, and motorcycles. Low-quality gasolines can cause a noise called "knocking" in an internal combustion engine. In an internal-combustion engine, the fuel is mixed with air and burned. The burning should take place smoothly. Knocking occurs when the fuel burns too quickly and explodes. Knocking weakens the engine and causes it to lose power.

Gasoline is a mixture of hydrocarbons and other substances such as toluene and benzene. (*See* HYDROCARBON.) Some hydrocarbons cause bad knocking while others cause hardly any. Therefore gasoline manufacturers have devised a scale called octane rating. The higher the octane rating, the less likely is the gasoline to cause knocking. Iso-octane is a hydrocarbon that causes hardly any knocking. It is given an octane rating of 100. Normal-heptane, another hydrocarbon, causes bad knocking. It is given an octane rating of 0. Suppose that an octane rating is required for a certain grade of gasoline. A mixture of iso-octane and normal-heptane is made up. The amounts of the two hydrocarbons are altered until it has the same tendency to knock as the gasoline. The octane rating of the gasoline is equal to the percentage of iso-octane in the mixture. For example, a high-grade gasoline might have an octane rating of 98. Then it knocks as much as a mixture of 98 percent iso-octane and 2 percent normal-heptane.

M.E./J.M.

The octopus (below) has no outside shell. It has eight sucker-covered arms, or tentacles, which spread out from its soft, baglike body. Most octopuses live in warm water.

OCTOPUS (äk′ tə pəs) The octopus is a marine mollusk belonging to the class of cephalopods. There are about 150 types of octopuses. They live mainly along the coasts of Hawaii, North America, and the West Indies. Octopuses are also found in the China and Mediterranean seas. Octopuses have no outside shells, and their eight sucker-covered arms (called tentacles) spread out from a soft, baglike body. Most octopuses are only a little bigger than a person's fist. But the largest ones may measure 8.5 m [28 ft] from the tip of one tentacle to the tip of another on the opposite side of the body.

The octopus has large, shiny eyes and strong, hard jaws. Most octopuses feed on crabs, lobsters, and other crustaceans. Such animals are caught by the octopus's tentacles. If an octopus loses a tentacle, a new one grows in its place. The octopus has the most highly developed brain of all the invertebrates.

When disturbed, the octopus darts away, squirting out a black fluid. This fluid forms a dark cloud to confuse the attacker and hide the octopus's retreat. Also, when an octopus becomes excited, it changes color, becoming brown, gray, red, purple, blue, white, and sometimes even striped. Many types of octopuses change color to blend in with their surroundings. (*See* CAMOUFLAGE.)

J.J.A./C.S.H.

OERSTED, HANS CHRISTIAN *See* ELECTROMAGNETISM.

OHM (ōm) The ohm is the unit of electrical resistance. Suppose that a wire has a resistance of one ohm. Then a potential difference of one volt produces a current of one ampere in the wire. The ohm is named after the German scientist Georg Ohm. (*See* OHM, GEORG.) The symbol for the ohm is the Greek letter Ω. It is called omega. *See also* RESISTANCE, ELECTRICAL.   M.E./L.L.R.

OHM, GEORG SIMON (1787–1854) Georg Ohm (ōm) was a German physicist. He made important discoveries in the study of electricity. His most famous discovery is now called Ohm's law. (*See* OHM'S LAW.) He discovered it in 1827. Ohm's law shows that the size of the current in a substance depends on its resistance and the voltage. The unit of resistance, the ohm, is named after him. He also studied sound. He helped to found the science of acoustics. (*See* ACOUSTICS.)
                    M.E./D.G.F.

OHM'S LAW (ōmz lò) Ohm's law is a very important law in electricity. If a potential difference is placed across a substance, then an electric current can flow through it. Ohm's law states that the size of the current depends on two things. It depends on the size of the potential difference. It also depends on the electrical resistance of the substance. (*See* RESISTANCE, ELECTRICAL.) This is written as:
$$I = V/R.$$
I is the current measured in amperes. V is the potential difference measured in volts. R is the resistance measured in ohms. The current increases as the potential difference increases. But it decreases as the resistance increases. The law is only accurate for good conductors, such as metals. Also, the temperature has to remain the same for the law to hold. This is because the resistance varies with temperature. In practice, a current heats up a substance in which it flows. This causes the resistance to increase. Therefore, Ohm's law is never strictly accurate. The law is named after the German scientist Georg Ohm. (*See* OHM, GEORG.)   M.E./J.T.

OIL SHALE (òil shāl) Oil shale is a fine-grained sedimentary rock that ranges in color from tan to black. It contains a waxy substance called kerogen. Kerogen forms from decayed organic material and has a low oil content. Petroleum can be extracted from oil shale at great expense.

Oil shale may become a more important source of petroleum as the modern energy crisis deepens. Some scientists think that oil shale represents an early stage in petroleum formation. Deposits of oil shale are found in Colorado, Utah, and Wyoming. *See also* PETROLEUM.   J.M.C./W.R.S.

OLEFIN (ō′ lə fən) Hydrocarbons are compounds in which the molecules contain atoms of carbon and hydrogen. One class of hydrocarbon is called the olefins. They are also known as alkenes.

The atoms in a molecule are held together by chemical bonds. (*See* CHEMICAL BOND.) In an olefin, two of the carbon atoms are held together by a double bond. The most simple olefin is ethene ($CH_2{=}CH_2$). The next simplest is propene ($CH_3{-}CH{=}CH_2$). Olefins can contain many atoms, but they must have just one double bond. Simple olefins are gases. Olefins with more carbon atoms are liquids. If they have still more carbon atoms, they are waxy solids.

Olefins are obtained from petroleum. The double bond in an olefin can be opened in a chemical reaction. Then, other atoms or groups of atoms become attached to the two carbon atoms. Because of this, they are reactive substances. They are used as fuels and to manufacture other chemicals, such as alcohols. They are also used to make plastics, such as polyethylene and polypropylene. These plastics are made by a process called

The olm is blind salamander found in underground streams in caves in eastern Europe. The olm is an albino and has no color pigmentation.

polymerization. (*See* POLYMERIZATION.) In polymerization, the double bond is opened up and the molecules link up with each other. In this way, very long chain molecules are formed. This results in a plastic.   M.E./J.M.

OLIGOCENE EPOCH (äl′ i gō señ′ ep′ək) The Oligocene epoch is the division of the Tertiary period that began about 38 million years ago and lasted about 12 million years.

The Oligocene epoch was characterized by a temperate to subtropical climate. Extensive grasslands existed on the major continents. The Oligocene saw the appearance of the mesohippus, a prehistoric ancestor of the modern horse. Primitive apes developed at this time. Many modern mammals, including camels, cats, dogs, rodents, and elephants, appeared. *Baluchitherium*, the largest land mammal of all time, thrived during the Oligocene.

Many of the abundant insects of this epoch have been preserved as fossils in amber. Lignite deposits also formed during the Oligocene epoch. *See also* GEOLOGICAL TIME SCALE; TERTIARY PERIOD.

   J.M.C./W.R.S.

OLIVE FAMILY The olive (äl′ iv) family includes about 400 species of shrubs, trees, and climbing plants. They are dicotyledons and are mostly tropical and subtropical. The leaves are opposite or whorled. (*See* LEAF.) The four-petal flowers grow in clusters. Some species, such as jasmine and lilac, have fragrant flowers. Other species, such as the varieties of ash, are popular trees in North America and Europe. Forsythia is a shrub grown for its beautiful, bright yellow flowers.

The olive tree (*Olea europaea*) is native to Mediterranean countries. It reaches a height of 10 m [33 ft] and has greenish gray bark and leaves. Some olive trees are at least 2,000 years old. The fruit, a large, purplish black olive, is a popular food. Olives are sometimes harvested and bottled while they are still green. Although some olives are grown in California, most are produced in Italy and Spain. Olive oil is squeezed from the fruit and is used for cooking and salads.

   A.J.C./M.H.S.

OLM (ōlm) The olm is a blind salamander that lives in caves in eastern Europe. Because there is no light in the caves, the olm does not need eyes. It feeds by feeling for and catching small animals swimming near it. The olm is an albino and has no color pigmentation. (*See* ALBINO; PIGMENTATION.) Since there is no light, there is no need for colors.

The olm resembles the Texas blind cave salamander which is an endangered species. It lives in water, breathing through external gills. An olm may live for more than 25 years. *See also* GILLS; SALAMANDER.

   S.R.G./R.L.L.

OMNIVORE (äm′ ni vōr′) An omnivore is an animal that eats both plants and animals. Human beings are omnivorous because they eat meat, fish, vegetables, and fruit. Other omnivorous animals are bears, pigs, badgers, and certain birds. *See also* CARNIVORE; HERBIVORE.   S.R.G./R.J.B.

ONION (ən′ yən) The onion (*Allium cepa*) is a biennial herbaceous plant belonging to the lily family. Many varieties are planted as seeds which produce leaves growing inside of each other. Near the end of the first growing season, food is stored in an underground bulb. (*See* BULB AND CORM.) It is this bulb that is the familiar vegetable called an onion. Some plants produce small bulblets among the leaves. Each bulblet can grow into a new plant. In the second year, clusters of greenish flowers are produced.

Onions have a strong, sharp taste and odor because of an oil. This oil forms a vapor if the onion is cut or peeled. This vapor irritates nerves in the nose, causing the eyes to start tearing. Onions have little food value themselves, but are often added to foods for flavoring. Scallions are young onions that have been harvested early in the first growing season, before bulbs have formed. *See also* LILY FAMILY. A.J.C./F.W.S.

ONYX (än′ iks) Onyx is a name generally applied to a type of marble. This marble is characterized by the presence of straight, colored bands. The word onyx is also applied to agate, a fine-grained type of quartz. (*See* AGATE.)

Onyx marble, also called Mexican onyx, is a type of calcite marble. It is found on the walls of caves. Mexican onyx ranges in color from white to green, brown, and red. Much of this soft onyx marble is dyed and cut into gemstones or used as a decorative stone.

Onyx of quartz or agate is harder than onyx marble and takes a high polish. It may be dyed black and white, red and white, green and white, and other colors. Jewelers refer to dyed, single color agate as onyx. When speaking simply of onyx, jewelers mean the black stone. J.J.A./R.H.

OOGONIUM (ō ə gō′ nē əm) An oogonium is a one-celled female reproductive structure found in some algae and fungi. It produces eggs for sexual reproduction. It is similar to, but much simpler than, the multicellular archegonium or pistil found in many other plants. *See also* GAMETE; REPRODUCTION. A.J.C./M.H.S.

OOZE (üz) Ooze is the muddy deposit found on the ocean floor. There are two main types of ooze: terrigenous and oceanic.

Terrigenous ooze is found along coastlines. Some of it was originally part of the coast, but was worn away by waves and ocean currents. (*See* COAST; EROSION.)

Oceanic ooze consists of the shells, skeletons, and other remains of small marine animals and plants. Diatom ooze comes from the microscopic diatom plants or algae. Diatom ooze has a high silica content. It is widespread in the southern oceans. The shells of foraminiferida, a group of tiny sea creatures, make up the ooze found in many shallow regions of the oceans. Radiolarian ooze contains the siliceous remains of radiolaria, another tiny sea creature. Radiolarian ooze is found in parts of the Pacific and Indian Oceans. Large parts of the Pacific Ocean's floor are covered with red clay.

Ooze also refers to the muddy deposits on the bottoms of rivers, ponds, and other bodies of water. *See also* PLANKTON. J.M.C./C.R.N.

OPAL (ō′ pəl) Opal is a gemstone noted for its opalescence, or showy play of colors. The most prized of these stones are the brilliant black opals of New South Wales, Australia. The best black opals show a play of several colors, with flashes of blue, green, red, and yellow. Other types of opal include the yellow or orange-red "fire opal," the rainbow-colored "harlequin opal," and the white opal. Opal is the birthstone for October.

Unlike most gemstones, opal is not found in the form of crystals. It is found in irregular patches, often filling cavities in rocks.

Chemically, opal consists of hydrated silica (silica and water). Most scientists believe the color flashes of opal are caused by the

Opals (above) consist of layers of silica. Refraction of light in different directions causes the flashing play of colors in these gems.

water. Each layer of silica in an opal has a slightly different water content and hence a different index of refraction. In other words, it bends light at a different angle—the angle varies according to the amount of water in the layer. According to most scientists, these different bendings break up the light that strikes the stone into a rainbow of colors.

J.J.A./R.H.

OPAQUE PROJECTOR (ō pāk′ prə jek′ tər) A projector is a machine that is used for producing an image on a screen. If an ordinary projector light is shown through an object such as a ''lantern slide'' or a photographic transparency and onto a screen to form an image. An opaque projector is a different sort of projector. It can produce an image on a screen of an opaque object. An object is opaque if you cannot see through it.

Therefore an ordinary projector cannot produce an image of an opaque object. In an opaque projector, light is shown onto the object. The object reflects the light. The reflected light is then focused by a lens onto the screen. An opaque projector is also known as an epidiascope. *See also* PROJECTOR.

M.E./S.S.B.

OPOSSUM (ə päs′ əm) The opossum is a member of a family of mammals living in the Western Hemisphere. Opossums are marsupials, mammals that carry their young about in the mother's pouch after birth. There are many species of opossums. Most of them live in Central and South America.

The common opossum (*Didelphis marsupialis*), also called the Virginia opossum, is the only kind of opossum found in the United States. This species has grayish white hair, a long snout, and big hairless ears. It is about the same size as a house cat. The common opossum can hang upside down by wrapping its prehensile tail around the branch of a tree.

Opossums hunt at night. They eat almost any kind of animal or plant food. When in danger, opossums lie motionless, appearing to be dead. This is how the term "playing possum" originated.   J.J.A./R.J.B.

The opossum's prehensile tail allows it to hang upside down from tree branches.

OPTICAL ILLUSION (äp' ti kəl il ü' zhən) An optical illusion is a false impression in the brain of what the eyes are seeing. It is not the same as a hallucination. In a hallucination, a person is quite sure that he or she can see something, or hear something, when in fact it does not exist. An optical illusion is a misleading sensation produced by something that really does exist.

Optical illusions are quite normal. They are experienced by every normal person. Experiments have shown that some animals experience them too. Even pigeons and fish can be misled by appearances.

The best-known optical illusions involve size and shape. Position, color, and movement can also be misleading. In the Müller-Lyer arrow illusion, the vertical lines are actually the same length. However, the line with the arrowheads pointing outwards appears shorter than the line with the arrowheads

In the distorted square and distorted circle illusions (above), a square and a circle are made to seem distorted by being placed on patterned backgrounds. This is an optical illusion.

In the circle illusion, the circle surrounded by smaller circles looks larger than the one surrounded by larger ones, but both are the same size.

pointing inwards. In the circle illusion, the circle surrounded by smaller circles appears larger than the circle surrounded by larger ones. In fact the central circles are identical in size. The eye is deceived by the relative sizes of the outside circles.

Illusions of shape occur when lines or circles are drawn on or near backgrounds with a strong pattern. A circle or square can be made to appear distorted by placing it on a background with a clear, regular pattern.

Illusions of movement may occur when the eye is misled by a series of events happening one after another. This illusion is used in street advertising signs. A series of electric light bulbs switched on and off in sequence can be made to appear like a moving pattern. In fact, there is no movement at all.

We all have to learn what it is we are really seeing. When we are very young, we cannot estimate distances and sizes. Experience gradually teaches us how angles, colors, and brightness are affected by distance. We learn about perspective. As we grow up, we unconsciously use our past visual experience to interpret what we see. However, the brain can be deceived. As an example, everyone becomes used to the fact that the sides of a road, or the tracks of a railway, seem to draw closer and closer together in the distance. Straight lines coming together like this become a clue to distance. Whenever a person sees lines meeting at a similar angle, even drawn on flat paper, the meeting point is unconsciously thought of as being further away from the eye. This is the basis of many optical illusions.

In common illusions, the brain interprets lines and patterns as being perspective drawings. But not all of the drawing fits into the same perspective, so parts are seen as being distorted. The brain tries to find perspective where none is meant to be.

Estimating distances and the true size of objects go together. We know that a ship seen miles away at sea is not really just an inch long. Yet looking at unfamiliar objects can be

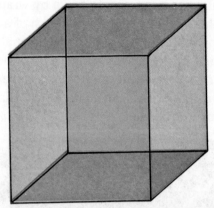

In this cube, either of the squarelike faces can appear to be nearest to the observer.

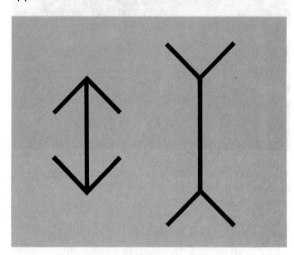

In the Müller-Lyer arrow illusion (above), both the vertical lines are the same length, but the one on the left seems shorter because the arrow-heads are pointing outward.

The dark areas (above) can be seen as the background to a vase shape, or as two facing profiles.

very misleading. If the distance is not known, the brain can be easily deceived about size.

D.M.H.W./S.S.B.

OPTICS (äp′ tiks) Optics is the branch of physics that studies the nature and properties of light. It also studies optical instruments such as telescopes and microscopes.

If light can travel through a substance, then the substance is said to be transparent. Glass, water, and air are all transparent substances. The substance in which light is traveling is called the medium. When a ray of light travels from one medium to another, it is sometimes bent. This effect is called refraction. If light cannot travel through a substance, then the substance is said to be opaque. Metal and wood are opaque. A ray of light bounces off an opaque surface. This is called reflection. Reflection and refraction are two very important subjects in optics.

Reflection When a ray of light strikes an opaque object, it is partially reflected. In fact, no substance is completely opaque. A small amount of light is always absorbed. The line at right angles to the surface where the ray hits is called the normal. The reflected ray makes the same angle to the normal as the incoming or incident ray. If the surface is flat and smooth, then all the rays are reflected at the same angle. The surface then looks shiny and can be used as a mirror. If the surface is rough, the rays are reflected at different angles by different parts of the surface. This is because the angle between the incident ray and the normal varies along the surface. This makes the surface look dull.

A mirror is capable of forming an image of an object. This is because its surface is smooth and it reflects a large amount of light. Different mirrors produce different kinds of images. A mirror that is curved outwards at the center is called a convex mirror. Its image is called a virtual image. A virtual image cannot be projected onto a screen. Flat mir-rors also produce a virtual image. A mirror that is curved inward at the center is called a concave mirror. It produces either a virtual or a real image. A real image can be projected onto a screen. If two parallel rays hit a mirror, they meet at a point called the focal point. The distance from the focal point to the center of the mirror is called the focal length of the mirror. (*See* MIRROR; REFLECTION OF LIGHT.)

Refraction Suppose that a ray of light hits a block of glass. Glass is transparent and most of the light passes through. A small part of it is reflected off the surface. If the ray hits the surface at an angle to the normal, then it is bent towards the normal. This is called refraction. Refraction occurs whenever light passes from one medium to another.

An important part of optics is the study of lenses. A lens is a curved piece of glass that causes a ray of light to bend as it passes through. Like mirrors, lenses can produce either real or virtual images. If the lens is thinner in the middle, it is called a diverging lens. Diverging lenses produce a virtual image. If the lens is thicker in the middle, it is called a converging lens. It can produce either a real or a virtual image. Lenses also have focal lengths.

Lenses can have a number of faults. These are known as aberrations. In an optical instrument, aberrations have to be corrected because they distort the image. For example, different colors of light are refracted in different amounts. Ordinary light is a mixture of different colors. This tends to blur the image and cause it to be colored at the edges. This is called chromatic aberration. Spherical aberration is caused by the shape of the lens. A lens should bring all points of an image into focus at the same distance from the lens. In spherical aberration, rays from the edge of the lens are focused at a different distance from the rest of the rays. This causes blurring at the edges of the image. Another kind of aberration is called astigmatism. In astigmatism, if a

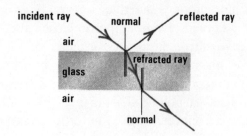

A light ray is reflected from the surface of a glass block, and refracted as it passes through the block.

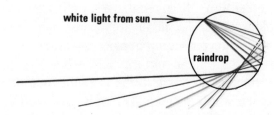

Sunlight is refracted by raindrops and splits up into its component colors to form a rainbow.

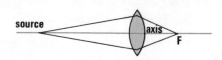

Light rays spread out from an object and are refracted by a convex lens to meet and form an image. The distance from the object to the lens is denoted by u, and the distance of the image from the lens by v.

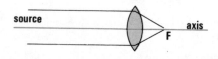

If the object is at infinity, the image forms at a distance equal to the focal length, f, of the lens. The distances are related by the formula

$$\frac{1}{u} + \frac{1}{v} = \frac{1}{f}.$$

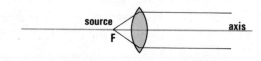

If the object is at the focal length, the image forms at infinity.

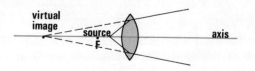

A virtual image forms if the object is nearer to the lens than the focal length.

horizontal line in an image is in focus, a vertical line will not be. This is done by using a number of different lenses in combination. (*See* ABERRATION.)

Interference Light is made up of waves. Like all waves, light waves have crests (high points) and troughs (low points). They also have a wavelength. This is the distance between one crest and the next. Two waves can combine to form a single wave. This effect is called interference. Suppose two waves have the same wavelength. If their crests and troughs coincide, a large combined wave is formed. This is called constructive interference. If the crests of one wave coincide (come together) with the troughs of another, the waves cancel each other out. This is called destructive interference. Interference is used in an optical instrument called the interferometer. (*See* INTERFEROMETER.)

M.E./A.I.

ORANGE (òr′ inj) The orange is the most important of the citrus fruits. It belongs to genus *Citrus* of the rue family. Oranges grow on trees in warm climates. The trees reach a height of about 10 m [33 ft] and usually live for more than 80 years. The leaves are large, shiny, and dark green in color. The fragrant, white flowers are known as orange blossoms, and have long been associated with marriage and weddings. The fruit is a specialized berry with 10 to 15 segments surrounding a central pith. (*See* FRUIT.) These segments are filled with juice that is rich in sugar, citric acid, minerals, and vitamins. Oranges are an especially good source of vitamin C. (*See* VITAMIN.) A protective rind surrounds the fruit. The rind contains glands which produce orange oil.

There are three main types of oranges: sweet, or common, oranges (*Citrus sinensis*); bitter, or Seville, oranges (*Citrus aurantium*); and tangerines, or mandarin oranges (*Citrus reticulata*). Most of the oranges grown in the

United States are sweet oranges. Florida produces about five times as many oranges as its closest competitor, California. Texas and Arizona also produce large orange crops. Most of the California oranges are sold as fresh fruit, whereas about 75% of the Florida oranges are processed into frozen concentrate. Florida oranges differ from California oranges in several ways. Florida oranges have thinner skins, more juice, more sugar, less acid, and less natural orange color. Their color is sometimes enhanced by the use of red food dyes. Oranges from throughout the country are commonly treated with ethylene gas to bring out the orange color and eliminate any green color.

The United States produces more than 9 billion kg [20 billion lb] of oranges and tangerines every year. Most of the sweet oranges grown in the United States are Valencia oranges. Valencia oranges have a relatively thin rind and few, if any, seeds. They are usually a bright, golden orange color. Another popular variety is the navel orange. The navel orange is actually two fruits in one. There is a tiny, undeveloped fruit embedded at one end of the larger, juicy fruit. This produces the characteristic ''navel'' appearance.

Bitter oranges are often grown for use as rootstocks in grafting sweet oranges or other citrus fruits. (*See* VEGETATIVE PROPAGATION.) The rinds are sometimes used to make bitter marmalade. The flowers are sometimes processed into the French perfume, Eau de Cologne.

Tangerines are smaller than the other oranges. They are flattened at the ends. Tangerines have thin, reddish orange rinds that are easily peeled. The segments are easy to separate and are filled with a sweet, tasty juice.

Oranges have many uses. They can be eaten as fresh fruits or squeezed for their juice. Oranges can be processed into frozen concentrate or dry powder. They are used to flavor soft drinks, cakes, cookies, candies, and many other foods. The rinds can be used to make marmalade *See also* CITRUS FRUIT; RUE FAMILY.   A.J.C./F.W.S.

ORANGUTAN (ə rang′ ə tang′) The orangutan (*Pongo pygmaeus*) is a large, peaceful ape that lives only in the lowland tropical forests of Borneo and Sumatra. Its name comes from the Malay words meaning ''man of the woods.'' A male orangutan may grow to a height of 1.5 m [5 ft] and may weigh 90 kg [200 lb]. The female is usually about half this size. The male has fatty cheek flaps and a huge air sac that hangs over the chest from the throat. Orangutans have reddish brown hair. They have stocky bodies with short legs and long arms. When an orangutan stands upright, its arms reach to its ankles. Some males have an arm-spread of 2.3 m [7.5 ft], the longest of the apes.

Orangutans live alone or in groups of two to five. They live in the trees, climbing slowly and carefully from branch to branch. The orangutan is a herbivore and eats mostly fruits

A female orangutan and her baby are shown above. The baby orangutan nurses for more than a year and stays close to the mother for several years after that. Orangutans are rare animals.

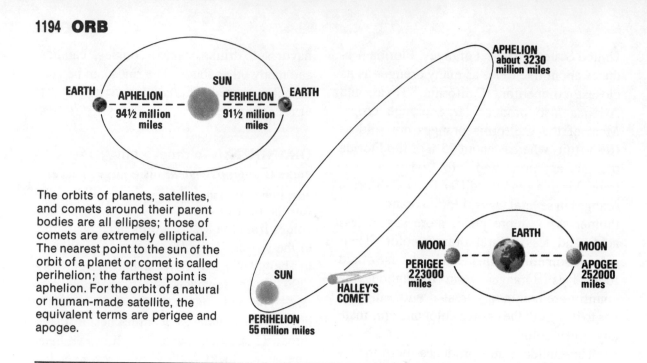

The orbits of planets, satellites, and comets around their parent bodies are all ellipses; those of comets are extremely elliptical. The nearest point to the sun of the orbit of a planet or comet is called perihelion; the farthest point is aphelion. For the orbit of a natural or human-made satellite, the equivalent terms are perigee and apogee.

and leaves. It builds a new nest every one or two nights. This nest is sometimes as high as 25 m [80 ft] in the trees. After mating and a gestation period of about 275 days, the female gives birth to one young. (*See* GESTATION PERIOD.) The baby orangutan nurses for more than a year and stays close to the mother for several years after that. Orangutans are sexually mature by the time they are 10 years old, and live for about 30 years.

Orangutans are considered to be rare animals because very few are left in the wild. They have been the victims of hunters and the growth of population which destroyed their natural living areas. *See also* APE.

A.J.C./J.J.M.

ORBIT (ȯr′ bət) An orbit is the path that one body follows around another larger body. A body follows an orbit because it is trapped in the gravitational field of the larger body. (*See* GRAVITY.) For example, the moon follows an orbit around the earth. Therefore, the moon is a satellite of the earth. When discussing the earth's orbit around the sun, the earth is a satellite.

In order for a satellite to escape the gravi-

tational field of the body it is orbiting, the satellite must reach a speed known as the escape velocity. Space scientists must calculate the escape velocity necessary for a spacecraft to leave the earth's gravitational field. (*See* SPACE TRAVEL.)

Most orbits are elliptical (oval-shaped), although some planets have nearly circular orbits around the sun.

In the orbit of a body around the sun, the closest point that it comes to the sun is called the perihelion. The most distant point is called the aphelion. Orbiting bodies around the sun include planets and comets.

In the orbit of a body around the earth or other planets, the closest point is called the perigee. The most distant point is called the apogee. Orbiting bodies around the earth include the moon and artificial satellites. *See also* COMET; MOON; PLANET; SATELLITE.

J.M.C./C.R.

ORCHID FAMILY (ȯr′ kəd) The orchid family includes 400 to 800 genera with 15,000 to 35,000 species of monocotyledonous flowering plants. Most grow in tropical, subtropical, or temperate areas. These herbaceous plants are perennial. Most orchids provide their own food by means of photosynthesis. (*See* PHOTOSYNTHESIS.) Some, however, rely on decaying organic material as a source of nutrition. (*See* SAPROPHYTE.) Others live symbiotically with mycorrhiza, a root fungus. (*See* FUNGUS; SYMBIOSIS.)

The color of the orchid flower varies from white to deep purple, depending on the species. Some orchids have streaks or spots of color in the petals. The flower has three sepals and three petals. One of these petals is highly modified and is called a lip. The lip may be any of several shapes, depending on the species. There is a club-shaped reproductive column in the center of the blossom. This column is actually fused stamens and pistils. (*See* FLOWER.)

Each species of orchid is pollinated by a specific kind of insect. The flower is usually modified in some way to attract that insect. The lip of some orchids, for example, looks like a female insect. (*See* MIMICRY.) When a male insect tries to mate with the flower, it brushes against the reproductive column, picking up or passing on pollen for pollination. (*See* POLLINATION.) In many cases, the lip has special coloring which attracts and guides the insect. Some orchid flowers produce more than two million tiny seeds, each of which can grow into a new plant. (*See* DISPERSION OF PLANTS.)

Orchids that grow in temperate areas usually grow in the ground. Most tropical orchids, however, grow high up in the trees. (*See* EPIPHYTE.) When a tiny orchid seed, carried by the wind, lodges in the bark of a tree, the seed germinates. (*See* GERMINATION.) It sends out a mass of roots which hangs in the air. Some of these roots have a special spongelike coating, called velamen, which absorbs moisture from the air.

A.J.C./M.H.S.

ORDER (ȯrd′ ər) An order, in the classification of living organisms, is a subdivision of a

Most orchids (above) grow in tropical, subtropical, or temperate areas. The color of the orchid flower varies from white to deep purple.

class. It is made up of a group of related families. *See also* CLASS; CLASSIFICATION OF LIVING ORGANISMS; FAMILY.   A.J.C./C.R.N.

ORDOVICIAN PERIOD (ȯrd′ ə vish′ ən)

The Ordovician period is the division of the Paleozoic era that began about 500 million years ago and lasted about 65 million years.

About two-thirds of North America and most of Scandinavia were covered by shallow water during the Ordovician. No life on land is known to have existed, although life in the seas flourished. Algae were plentiful. Other marine creatures included trilobites, corals, brachiopods, and graptolites. Jawless fish, the first known vertebrates, appeared during this period. Deposits of oil, lead, and zinc formed.

Some geologists suggest that eastern South America, Africa, the Indian peninsula, Australia, and Antarctica may have been close together during the Ordovician period. This theory is supported by the unusual distribution of Ordovician fossils throughout the world. *See also* CONTINENTAL DRIFT; GEOLOGICAL TIME SCALE; PALEOZOIC ERA.

J.M.C./W.R.S.

ORE (ōr)

Many minerals contain metals that are combined with other elements. Minerals from which pure metals can be extracted (removed) are called ores. Also, ores are any materials that can be mined at a profit, not just ores from which pure metals can be extracted. Such ores include salt, gypsum, and limestone.

"Native metals" and "compound ores" are the two types of ores. In native metals, the valuable mineral occurs as a pure metal. It is not chemically combined with other substances. Gold, silver, and platinum often occur as native metals. Compound ores include "oxides," which are compounds of metals with oxygen, "carbonates," which are compounds of metals with carbon and oxygen, and "sulfides," which are com-

pounds of metals with sulfur. *See also* MINING; MINERAL; ROCK.   J.J.A./R.H.

ORGAN (ȯr′ gən)

An organ is any part of an animal or plant that has a characteristic shape and structure. An organ also performs a particular function in an organism's life. For example, the heart is one of the most important organs in the human body. The root is a vital organ in higher plants. Several organs may function together as an organ system. The heart, for example, is part of the circulatory system. *See also* ANATOMY.

W.R.P./J.J.F.

ORGANELLE (ȯr′ gə nel′)

The organelle is a tiny structure found inside a living cell. Organelles perform special tasks that contribute to the working of cells. The most important organelles include: the nucleus, the cell's control center; the ribosomes, where proteins are manufactured; the mitochondria, where food is burned to provide energy; the endoplastic reticulum, the cell's internal transport system; and the Golgi apparatus, where substances to be secreted by the cell are packaged.

The cells of green plants include chloroplasts, where photosynthesis takes place, have external organelles, such as whiplike flagella. (*See* FLAGELLUM.)

W.R.P./C.R.N.

ORGANIC CHEMISTRY (ȯr gan′ ik kem′ ə strē)

There are two main classes of chemical compounds. One is called inorganic compounds and the other organic compounds. Organic chemistry studies the chemical properties of organic compounds.

Organic compounds are compounds that contain the element carbon. (*See* CARBON.) A few simple carbon compounds are classed as inorganic. For example, the gases carbon dioxide and carbon monoxide are inorganic. Carbon compounds are called organic because many of them are found in living organisms. Inorganic compounds are found in

EXAMPLES OF THE MAIN KINDS OF ORGANIC CHEMICALS

ALIPHATIC COMPOUNDS
have carbon atoms linked in *chains* which can be straight or branched

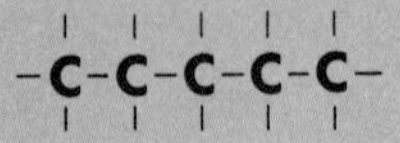

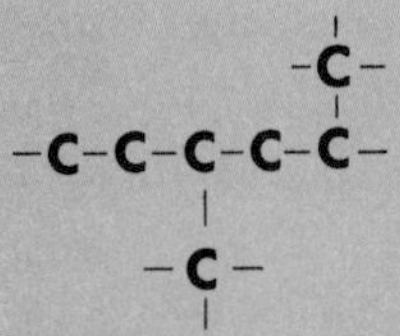

ALICYCLIC COMPOUNDS
have three or more carbon atoms linked as in aliphatic compounds but in *rings*

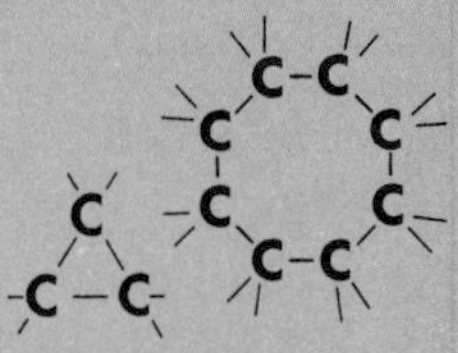

AROMATIC COMPOUNDS
have one or more BENZENE rings of six carbon atoms

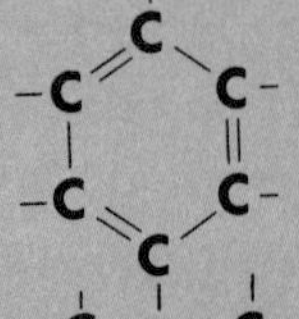

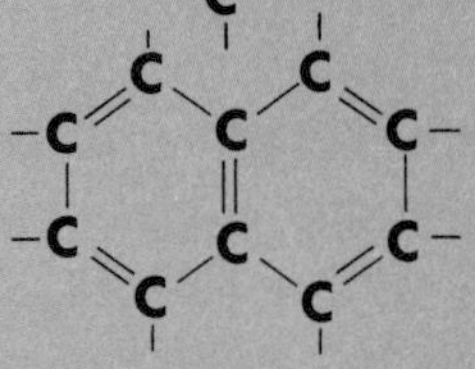

HETEROCYCLIC COMPOUNDS
have rings containing other atoms (X and Y) as well as those of carbon

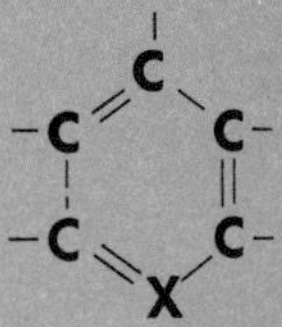

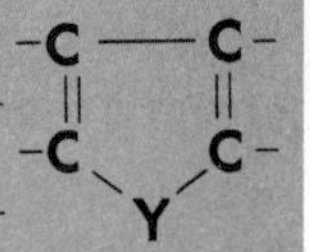

EXAMPLES: of Aliphatics | of Alicyclics | of Aromatics | of Heterocyclics

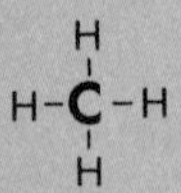

methane

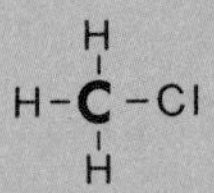

methyl chloride

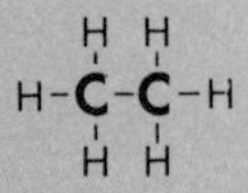

cyclopropane

benzene

pyrimidine

ethane

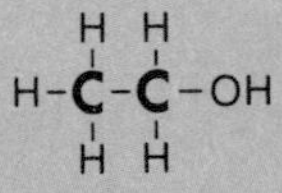

ethyl alcohol

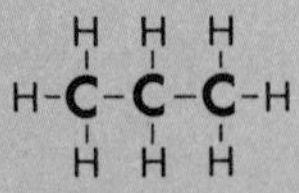

propane

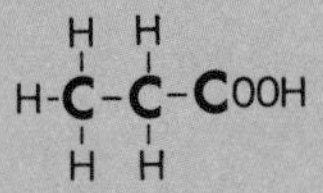

propionic acid

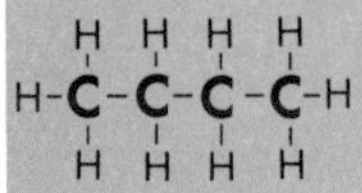

cyclohexane

phenol

furan

n-butane

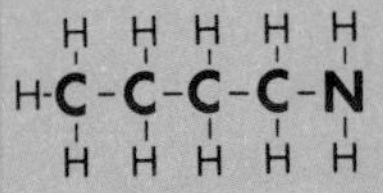

n-butylamine

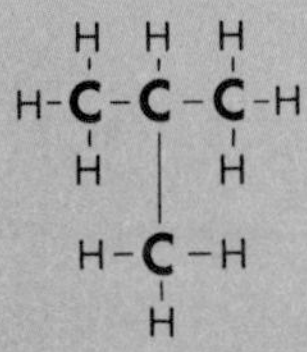

iso-butane

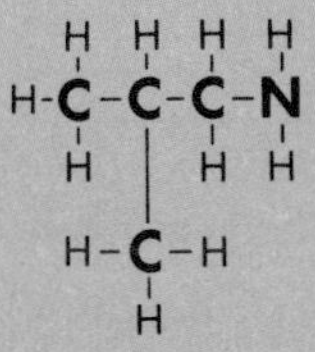

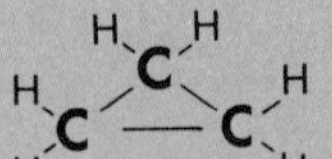

iso-butylamine

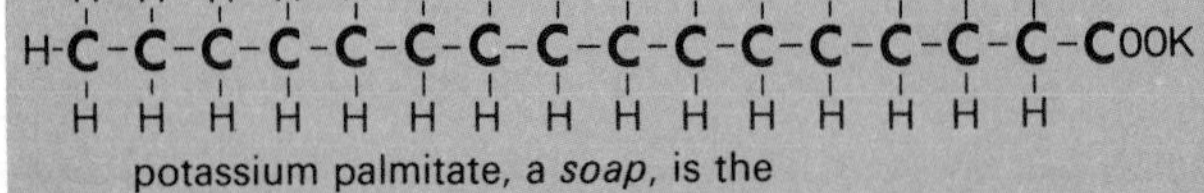

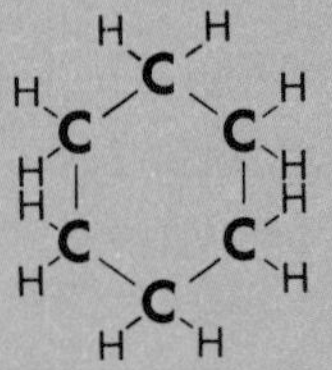

cyclohexanol

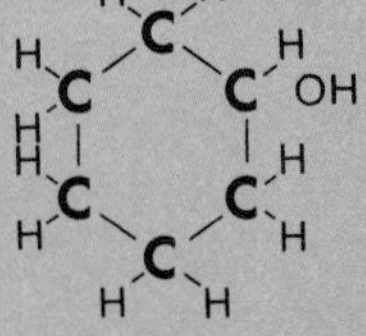

benzoic acid

potassium palmitate, a *soap*, is the potassium (K) salt of palmitic acid

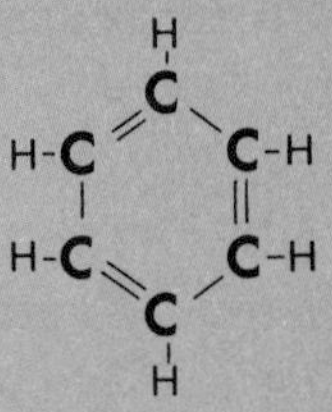

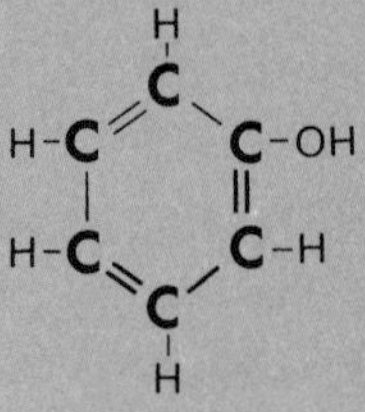

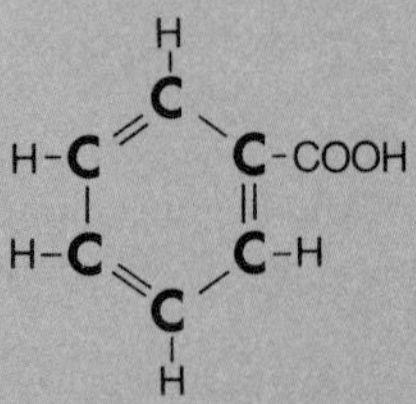

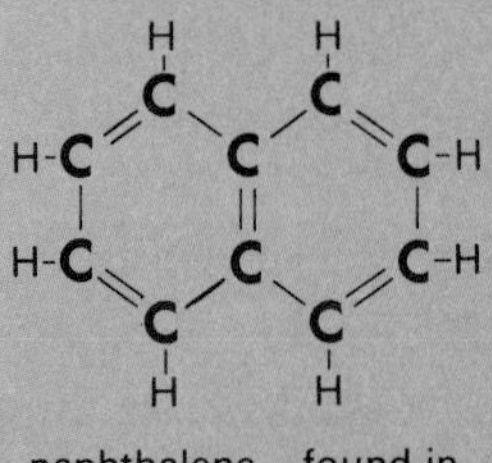

naphthalene—found in coal tar and petroleum

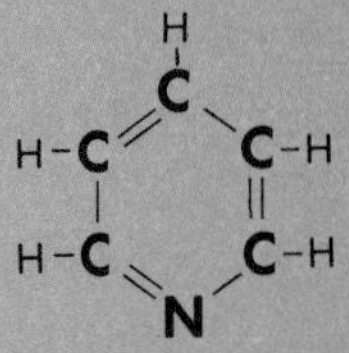

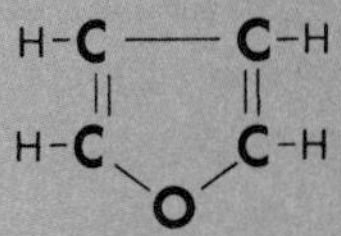

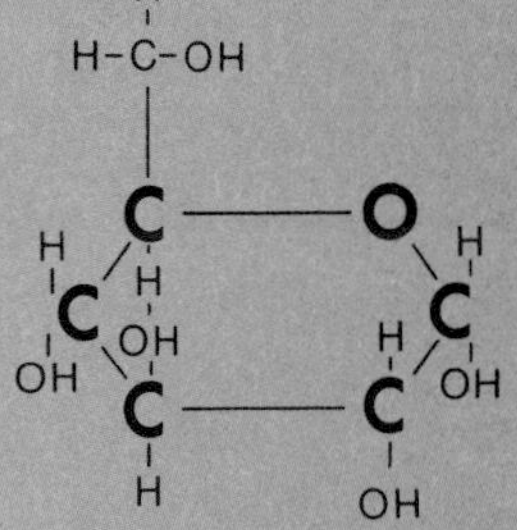

one form of the sugar glucose, important in the metabolism (body chemistry) of living organisms

minerals, the atmosphere, and so on. In the early 1800s, chemists thought that organic compounds did not obey the same laws as inorganic compounds. They thought that organic compounds could only be obtained from living organisms. Then, in 1828, the German chemist Friedrich Wöhler obtained an organic compound from an inorganic compound. He prepared urea from ammonium cyanate. Today many organic compounds are made from inorganic compounds, both in industry and in laboratories. However, many properties of organic compounds are different from those of inorganic compounds. Therefore organic chemistry is still treated as a separate branch of chemistry.

Most substances are made up of groups of atoms called molecules. (*See* MOLECULE.) Almost all organic compounds contain carbon atoms attached to each other either in rings or chains. Usually the carbon atoms are also attached to hydrogen atoms. Sometimes, though, they are attached to other atoms such as oxygen and nitrogen. Most inorganic molecules contain less than ten atoms. Many organic compounds contain large numbers of atoms, sometimes hundreds. These atoms can be arranged differently in the molecule. Compounds that have the same atoms but with a different arrangement are called isomers. They are very common in organic chemistry. (*See* ISOMER.)   M.E./J.M.

ORGANISM (òr′ gə niz′ əm) Organism is a general term for any particular form of life. Organisms are usually classified as either animals or plants. All organisms consist of one or many cells. Viruses, which do not consist of cells, are on the borderline between living and non-living matter. *See also* ANIMAL KINGDOM; PLANT KINGDOM.   W.R.P./C.R.N.

ORIOLE (ōr′ ē ōl′) The orioles are about 30 species of perching birds that belong to genus *Icterus*. They are closely related to the American blackbirds. The males are usually

black and yellow, or black and red with white spots. They are known for their warbled or whistled songs. The females are usually not as brightly colored and sing simpler songs. Orioles eat insects, sometimes prying them out of trees with their beaks. Most orioles live in warm, wooded areas. The northern oriole (*Icterus galbula*) lives all over the United States east of the Rocky Mountains. The eastern and western forms of this species differ in color.

In Europe and Asia, the orioles belong to an entirely different family, the Oriolidae. *See also* BLACKBIRD; PERCHING BIRD.

A.J.C./L.L.S.

ORION (ə rī′ ən) Orion, or the Great Hunter, is one of the brightest and most beautiful of the constellations. From December to April, it is visible in the night sky of the mid-northern hemisphere.

Orion contains many brilliant stars. They are said to form the shape of the mythical hunter Orion. It has two first magnitude stars: Betelgeuse and Rigel. Betelgeuse is a yellowish red color. Rigel is a blue giant in the hunter's knee. The three second magnitude stars that make up the hunter's belt seem to lie on the celestial equator. (*See* CELESTIAL SPHERE.) Below the belt is the Great Nebula of Orion. This huge mass of dust and gases can be seen from earth without a telescope. *See also* CONSTELLATION; MAGNITUDE.

J.M.C./C.R.

ORNITHOLOGY (òr′ nə thäl′ ə jē) Ornithology is the biological science that studies birds. It deals with all matters involving birds' lives, distribution, classification, and history. Ornithologists, the scientists who study birds, are interested in these animals' activities: mating, nesting, feeding, care of young, and migration.

People have been interested in birds since prehistoric times. Most of the early writings on birds were brief descriptions of, or stories about, birds. In the Middle Ages, people were interested in the birds that could be used for hunting. In the 18th and 19th centuries, scientists described and classified most known species of birds. In the late 19th and during the 20th centuries, many ornithologists concentrated on the anatomy, behavior, and ecology of birds. Much information about the distribution, activities, and migrations of birds has come through a technique known as banding. In banding, a small metal or plastic band is attached to the leg of a bird. Then the birds are set free. Amateur bird watchers throughout the world are able to supply scientists with information about the banded birds. In fact, ornithology is one of the few sciences that relies heavily on the observations of amateurs. Birds were first banded in the 19th century. Now, hundreds of thousands of birds are banded every year. *See also* BIRD; ZOOLOGY.   A.J.C./L.L.S.

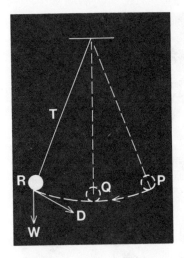

Given a push, the bob (weight) of a simple pendulum oscillates along an arc RQP. As it reaches the R end of the arc, the pull of gravity stops it. Tension of thread T gives downward pull W a sideways effect D, so the bob moves back to Q, gathering speed. It slows again at end of arc P.

OSCILLATION (äs′ ə lā′ shən) Oscillation is the type of movement made, for example, by a pendulum. Suppose that a pendulum is held to one side and then let go. It swings to the vertical (up-and-down) position and then carries on until it stops on the other side. It then returns through the vertical position and stops when it reaches its original position. This is called a single oscillation. The time taken for a single oscillation is called the period of oscillation. The number of single oscillations in a second is called the frequency of oscillation. (*See* FREQUENCY.) Another example of an oscillation is the movement of a guitar string when it is plucked. The string moves back and forth about its position when it is straight. All oscillations eventually die away. For example, as the pendulum swings, its maximum position from the vertical becomes smaller. This is called damping. It is caused by a number of different effects. The most important is the effect of gravity on the pendulum. The friction of the air also has an effect.   M.E./J.T.

OSCILLATOR (äs′ ə lā′ tər) Oscillators are electrical devices that change direct current into a signal of desired frequency (number of vibrations per second), or into alternating current. They are used in radio and television receivers and in other equipment. (*See* ALTERNATING CURRENT.)

An oscillator is actually a kind of amplifier that strengthens a signal and then feeds part of the amplified signal back into itself to make its own input. A capacitor is an electrical component that can store electric charge. (*See* CAPACITOR AND CAPACITANCE.) If the capacitor is connected to a coil of wire called an inductor, then it becomes discharged. An electric current flows first in one direction through the coil. Then it decreases and starts to flow in the other direction. It decreases some more and starts to flow in the first direction again. The current is said to oscillate. (*See* OSCILLATION.) However, the current dies away because of the resistance of the circuits. The oscillations can be kept up by feeding energy into the circuit. This is done by means of a transistor or a vacuum tube. This arrangement is called an oscillator. Another kind of oscillator is the crystal oscillator. Here a crystal of quartz does the work of the capacitor and the inductor. Crystal oscillators are often used in radio receivers. They are used because radio transmitters require a very exact frequency.   M.E./L.L.R.

An oscilloscope can be used to show the shape of a vibration, or oscillation, which can be changed into an electric signal.

OSCILLOSCOPE (ä sil′ ə skōp′) An oscilloscope is an electronic instrument. It is used to show the vibration, or oscillation, of an electric signal. (*See* OSCILLATION.) An oscilloscope contains a cathode-ray tube similar to the tube found in television sets. (*See* CATHODE-RAY TUBE.) The cathode-ray tube contains a screen. The shape of the vibration is shown on the screen. The shape is produced by a beam of particles called electrons. This beam strikes the screen of the oscilloscope and produces a spot of light. The beam moves along the screen and is deflected up or down as it moves. The deflection corresponds to the strength of the signal. The beam is made to move by two pairs of metal plates. The electric signal is applied to one pair of plates. One of the plates is above the beam and the other is below it. The signal causes the beam to move up or down. The other pair of plates lie on either side of the beam. A changing voltage is applied to the second pair of plates. This causes the beam to move across the screen from left to right. The beam can be speeded up or slowed down. This is done by changing

the voltage. When the beam reaches the end of the screen, it starts again on the left-hand side. An oscilloscope can also be used to show any kind of vibration, such as sound waves. In this case a device called a transducer is needed. It changes the sound waves into electric signals. (See TRANSDUCER.)

M.E./L.L.R.

OSMIUM (äz′ mē əm) Osmium (Os) is a hard, bluish white metallic element. Its atomic number is 76 and its atomic weight is 190.2. It melts at 3,050°C [5,520°F] and boils at 5,000°C [9,000°F]. Osmium is the densest substance known. Its density is 22.6 times that of water.

Osmium was discovered in 1803 by a British chemist Smithson Tennant. It is obtained from ores of platinum and nickel. Alloys of osmium are very hard and are good electrical conductors. They are used to make electrical parts, pen nibs, phonograph needles, bearings, and pivots.   M.E./J.R.W.

OSMOSIS (äz mō′ səs) Osmosis is the movement of a liquid through a semipermeable membrane from one solution into another solution. A semipermeable membrane is one that allows some, but not all, substances to pass through it. A solution is a mixture of a liquid (solvent) and dissolved particles (solute). (*See* SOLUTION AND SOLUBILITY.) In osmosis, the movement of a solvent is usually from a dilute solution (low concentration of solute) into a stronger, more concentrated solution (high concentration of solute). As a result, the stronger solution becomes more dilute. The rate of osmosis depends on the difference in the strengths of the solutions. The greater the difference, the faster the rate of osmosis. Osmosis continues until both solutions are of equal strength. When this state of equilibrium is reached, osmosis stops. (*See* EQUILIBRIUM.)

The membranes of a living cell are semipermeable. (*See* CELL.) Plants absorb water and dissolved minerals from the soil by osmosis. Osmosis is then used to move the water (and dissolved minerals) through the plant, cell by cell. Osmosis also maintains turgor pressure. Turgor pressure is the pressure of water in the cell. It gives the cell form and strength. When there is a decrease in turgor pressure, the plant will seem wilted and will not have its regular stiffness. Turgor pressure changes are responsible for some types of plant movement. (*See* MOVEMENT OF PLANTS.)

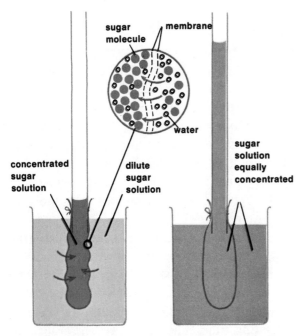

A bag (left) of sugar solution is tied to the end of a glass tube and immersed in a solution. The bag allows only water to pass through it. Water molecules (inset) pass into the bag. As the solution in the bag (right) becomes diluted, osmotic pressure forces the liquid up the tube.

In the human body, osmosis allows the transfer of water and dissolved nutrients from the blood into the cells. It also helps remove wastes and excess water from the cells. (*See* HOMEOSTASIS.) Osmosis also causes the movement of wastes and excess water from the blood into the kidney. (*See* EXCRETION; KIDNEY.)

A type of reverse osmosis can be caused by adding pressure to the system. Normally,

in a system made up of solutions of seawater and fresh water separated by a semipermeable membrane, osmosis would cause the water to move from the fresh water into the salt water in an attempt to reach equilibrium. When pressure is applied to the seawater, however, the water moves out of that solution and into the fresh water. This process is sometimes used for emergency purification of seawater for drinking purposes. *See also* MEMBRANE.

A.J.C./C.R.N.

OSPREY (äs′ prā′) The osprey is a bird of prey that belongs to the family Pandionidae. It is often called the fish hawk. It may grow to lengths of 55 cm [22 in] and may have a wingspan of 135 cm [54 in]. The wings and back of the osprey are a chocolate brown. The underside of the body and the head are white. The bird has a dark band running across its eyes that looks like a mask.

Ospreys usually eat only fish. They dive into the water from heights as high as 45 m [150 ft]. Unlike the bald eagle and most other fish-eating birds of prey, ospreys will plunge completely underwater to catch a fish. Although they are not very common, ospreys are found all over the world and in most coastal and lake areas of North America.

The Long Island Sound area in the northeastern United States was at one time the largest North American breeding ground for ospreys. In the late 1960s, the birds almost disappeared from the area because of water

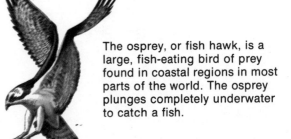

The osprey, or fish hawk, is a large, fish-eating bird of prey found in coastal regions in most parts of the world. The osprey plunges completely underwater to catch a fish.

pollution. Pesticides and other chemicals in the water had poisoned the fish they ate. Chemicals from the poisoned fish collected in the ospreys' bodies and caused their eggshells to be very thin. Most of the eggshells broke before the eggs were ready to hatch. In the 1970s, ornithologists began to bring healthy eggs from other areas to the nests on Long Island Sound. The eggs were hatched by new parents. Today, there is less poisoning of the waters and ospreys are becoming more numerous. S.R.G./L.L.S.

OSTRICH (äs' trich) The ostrich is the world's tallest bird. There is only one living species of ostrich (*Struthio camelus*). It grows to heights of 2.4 m [8 ft]. It cannot fly but it can run very fast. The wings and tail of the ostrich are white. The body of the male is black. The body of the female is brown. The feathers of the ostrich are unlike those of most birds. They resemble the fluffy down of young birds.

Ostriches are flightless birds which live in the grasslands and deserts of Africa and Arabia.

Ostriches live in the grasslands and deserts of Africa and Arabia. They were once very common. They were, however, often killed for their feathers. Today, large flocks are seen only in a few parts of eastern and southern Africa. S.R.G./L.L.S.

OTTER (ät' ər) The otter, a carnivorous mammal, is a member of the weasel family Mustilidae. Otters live close to water and spend most of their time in it. They are expert swimmers and divers, and they can stay under water for three or four minutes. Otters move awkwardly on land.

Otters live on every continent except Australia. Most otters weight from 4.5 to 14 kg [10 to 30 lb] and grow 0.9 to 1.4 m [3 to 4.5 ft] in length, including the tail. The giant otter of South America can grow 2 m [7 ft] long.

An otter has a small, flattened head, a long, thick neck, and a thick tail that narrows to a point. Special muscles enable the otter to tightly close its ears and nostrils to keep water out. Webbing between the toes helps the otter swim swiftly.

Otters have two layers of brownish gray fur. Long, coarse, outer hairs, called guard hairs, protect their short, thick underfur. The underfur traps air and keeps the otter's skin dry. Otters are solitary creatures, except at breeding time. They eat crayfish, crabs and various fish. They also eat clams, frogs, insects, snails, snakes, and, occasionally, waterfowl.

Otters usually live in burrows in riverbanks or under rocky ledges. Young otters do not swim until they are seven months old. People hunt otters for their beautiful underfur. W.R.P./J.J.M.

OVARY (ōv' rē) Ovary means "the place where eggs are made." In animals, the ovary produces ova (eggs) in the female. It also makes sex hormones which affect pregnancy and body shape. (*See* HORMONE; REPRODUCTION.)

The plant ovary is where the seeds are formed. (See CARPEL; FRUIT.)   C.M./J.J.F.

OVENBIRD (əv′ ən bərd′) The ovenbird is a wood warbler that belongs to the family Parulidae. It grows 12.5 cm [5 in] long. The back and wings of the ovenbird are olive brown. There is a rusty streak that can be raised in displays on the top of the head. The breast is white with black spots.

The ovenbird lives in the eastern half of North America. It nests on the ground and eats insects. It should not be confused with the ovenbirds of South and Central America. The birds are not related. Both birds were named ''ovenbirds'' by Europeans because each has a nest that resembles a type of oven. The North American ovenbird usually makes a covered nest of vegetation on the ground. The South American ovenbird uses sticks or mud and makes a very different type of nest.

S.R.G./L.L.S.

OWL (aŭl) An owl is a bird of prey that belongs to the order Strigiformes. It has a large head and eyes, short neck, broad wings, and sharp claws or talons. About 130 species of owls are found around the world. Eighteen species live in North America. Owls vary in size. The largest North American owl is the great gray owl. It grows 55 cm [22 in] long and has a wingspan of 150 cm [60 in]. The elf owl is the smallest owl in North America. It grows only 13.3 cm [5.25 in] long and has a wingspan of 37.5 cm [15 in].

Most owls are active at night. (*See* NOCTURNAL HABIT.) They have excellent eyesight and hearing which enable them to find and catch food. Their main food consists of rodents and other small mammals. During the night, owls fly quietly about, searching for food. During the day, they sit in trees and old buildings. Owls can be very helpful to farmers because they eat mice and rats that may harm crops. The call of many owls is an eerie ''who.''   S.R.G./L.L.S.

This illustration shows an owl, its talons outstretched, swooping down on a mouse. Owls are helpful to humans because they mainly eat rodents which damage food crops and food stores.

OXALIC ACID (äk sal′ ik as′ əd) Oxalic acid, $(COOH)_2 \cdot 2H_2O$, is a weak organic acid. It consists of white crystals. It is very poisonous and causes paralysis of the nervous system. Oxalic acid is found in some toadstools. Salts of oxalic acid are called oxalates. They are also poisonous. They are found in several plants including rhubarb leaves, dock, and wood sorrel. Oxalic acid is used in industry to make inks and dyes, and to bleach materials. It is also used to make polishes for metals. Plants are not used as a source of oxalic acid. It is manufactured by heating a substance called sodium formate. This causes it to change into sodium oxalate. Sulfuric acid is then added to obtain oxalic acid.   M.E./A.D.

OXIDATION AND REDUCTION Oxidation (äk′ sə dā′ shən) and reduction (ri dək′ shən) are two very important processes in chemical reactions. All atoms contain small particles called electrons. Sometimes the atoms of an element gain electrons from, or lose them to, other atoms. When this happens, the element is said to have an oxidation number, or an oxidation state. An element on its own has an oxidation number of 0. When it combines with another element, it gains or loses electrons. An electron has a negative charge. Therefore, if the atoms of an element each gain an electron, they gain a negative charge. Their oxidation number is now -1. If the atoms gain two electrons each, the oxidation number of the element becomes -2. In the same way, if the atoms of an element each lose an electron, they gain a positive charge. Its oxidation number is then $+1$. If the oxidation number of an element increases, it is said to be oxidized. If it decreases, it is reduced. For example, calcium and oxygen combine to form calcium oxide. When this happens, the calcium atoms each lose two electrons to the oxygen atoms. Therefore the oxidation number of the calcium increases from 0 to $+2$. It has been oxidized. The oxidation number of the oxygen changes from 0 to -2. It has been reduced.

The most common form of oxidation is when oxygen is added to an element or compound. That is why it is called oxidation. However, other elements can oxidize substances. For example, sodium combines with chlorine to form sodium chloride. The chlorine oxidizes the sodium because it gains electrons from it. In the same way, the sodium reduces the chlorine.

Substances that can oxidize other substances are called oxidizing agents. Many of them contain large amounts of oxygen in their molecules. Examples include oxygen (O_2), ozone (O_3), hydrogen peroxide (H_2O_2), and nitric acid (HNO_3). Other oxidizing agents, such as chlorine and fluorine, do not contain oxygen. Substances that reduce other substances are called reducing agents. Hydrogen and carbon are common reducing agents.

M.E./A.D.

OXIDE (äk′ sīd′) Oxides are compounds that contain oxygen and one other element. They include water, which is hydrogen oxide (H_2O); sand and quartz, which are silicon dioxide (SiO_2); and quicklime, which is calcium oxide (CaO). Many minerals consist of oxides. For example, the most important mineral of aluminum is bauxite which is aluminum oxide (Al_2O_3).

Some oxides, such as sulfur dioxide (SO_2) dissolve in water to form acids. They are called acidic oxides and are usually the oxides of nonmetals. Other oxides are called basic oxides. Some of these, such as sodium oxide (Na_2O) dissolve in water to form hydroxides. (*See* BASE.) Basic oxides combine with acids to form salts. This is called neutralization. (*See* NEUTRALIZATION.) Basic oxides are oxides of metals. Some oxides are both acidic and basic. They form salts with both acids and bases. They are called amphoteric oxides. Zinc oxide (ZnO) is an amphoteric oxide.

M.E./A.D.

OXYACETYLENE TORCH (äk′ sē ə set′ əl ən tòrch) An oxyacetylene torch is a very hot torch used for cutting and welding metals. Acetylene gas burns in oxygen to produce a very hot flame. The flame has a temperature of about 3,300°C [6,000°F]. Mixtures of oxygen and acetylene are used in oxyacetylene torches. They are used in welding and cutting metal. In welding, the heat of the flame melts two pieces of metal where they join. The molten (melted) metal mixes together. The pieces of metal are then allowed to cool and become solid. Because the metal from the two pieces has mixed, they are joined together.

An oxyacetylene torch has two main parts: a nozzle and a blowpipe. Acetylene and oxygen are kept separately, usually in two cylinders. The gases enter the blowpipe separately through two valves. They are mixed together and then leave the nozzle. The mixture is ignited (set on fire) as it leaves the nozzle. Different proportions of oxygen and acetylene are used for different metals.

For cutting metal, a slightly different kind of torch is used. The flame heats up the metal but does not heat it up enough to make it melt. A blast of high-pressure oxygen is directed at a certain point of the metal. The metal oxidizes away. The torch is slowly moved over the surface of the metal, cutting as it goes.

The flame produced when acetylene burns is very bright. For this reason, oxyacetylene mixtures are sometimes used for lighting. They are used, for example, in miners' lamps. *See also* WELDING AND CUTTING.

M.E./J.M.

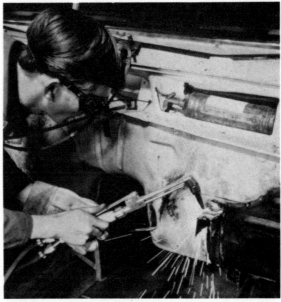

Oxyacetylene burners are used for cutting and welding metals and alloys. They produce an intensely hot flame by burning acetylene gas in oxygen.

OXYGEN (äk′ si jən) Oxygen is a chemical element. At room temperature it is a colorless, odorless gas. Its atomic number is 8 and its atomic weight is 15.9994. The boiling point of oxygen is − 182.9°C [−297.2°F]. It freezes at −218.4°C [−361.1°F].

Oxygen was discovered by two chemists working independently of each other. Carl Scheele, a Swedish chemist, discovered oxygen in about 1772. Then Joseph Priestley discovered oxygen in 1774 in England. Oxygen is one of the gases in the air. It makes up about 21 percent of the air. Oxygen is important to almost every form of life. People and land

The oxygen cycle in nature is shown below. It is linked with the carbon and nitrogen cycles.

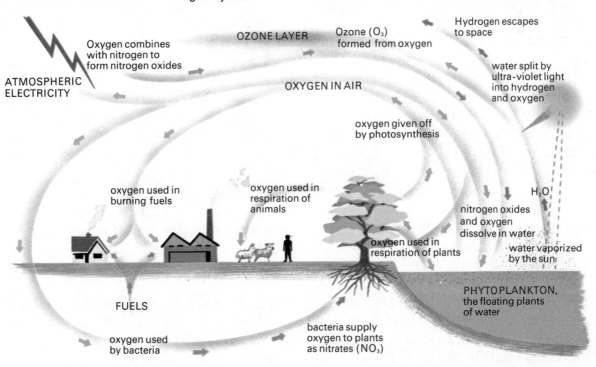

ATMOSPHERIC ELECTRICITY

Oxygen combines with nitrogen to form nitrogen oxides

OZONE LAYER

Ozone (O_3) formed from oxygen

Hydrogen escapes to space

water split by ultra-violet light into hydrogen and oxygen

OXYGEN IN AIR

oxygen given off by photosynthesis

oxygen used in burning fuels

oxygen used in respiration of animals

oxygen used in respiration of plants

nitrogen oxides and oxygen dissolve in water

H_2O

water vaporized by the sun

FUELS

PHYTOPLANKTON, the floating plants of water

oxygen used by bacteria

bacteria supply oxygen to plants as nitrates (NO_3)

animals take in oxygen from the air in their lungs. The oxygen then enters the blood and travels around the body. Water animals use the oxygen that is dissolved in the water. They have gills to obtain their oxygen. Plants absorb oxygen during the night. During the day they give off oxygen by photosynthesis. (*See* PHOTOSYNTHESIS.)

Pure oxygen is taken from the air. Air is first cooled until it liquefies. The different gases in the air boil at different temperatures. This allows the different gases to separate, in a process called fractional distillation. (*See* DISTILLATION.) Liquid oxygen is pale blue.

When substances react with oxygen, they are said to be oxidized. The body produces energy by oxidizing certain compounds. When fuels burn they are oxidized. Rust on iron is due to oxidation. (*See* OXIDATION AND REDUCTION.)

People suffering from severe illness may need more oxygen than normal. They are placed in oxygen tents and breathe pure oxygen. In welding, acetylene gas is combined with pure oxygen and burned. It gives a very hot flame. Liquid oxygen is used in space rockets to provide power. M.E./J.R.W.

OYSTER (oi′ stər) Oysters are a type of mollusk found in many warm or mild seas of the world. Oysters often live on the bottom of oceans, mostly in inlets near shore.

The oyster's shell is made up of two parts called valves. Oysters are known as bivalves (meaning two valves). A hinge at one end holds the valves together. One valve is deeper and larger than the other, and the oyster's body rests in it. The second (right) valve acts as a lid. The oyster usually keeps its valves slightly opened. If an enemy comes near, the oyster snaps the valves shut.

The mantle, a fleshy organ, lines the inside of the shell, surrounding the body organs. The mantle makes liquid substances that harden and form the shell, adding material to the shell. In this way, the shell be-

Oysters are often grown in shallow beds. An Australian oyster farm is shown above.

comes larger as the animal grows. Lines on the outside of the shell show the additions of this material from the mantle.

The oyster's soft body is a grayish mass of tissues containing the body organs. The oyster has no head. The animal uses its gills to breathe and capture food. Hairlike parts (cilia) of the gills gather tiny plants and animals (plankton) from the water and push them toward the oyster's mouth. The mouth is an opening at the narrowest part of the body.

Sometimes a grain of sand or similar object gets into the shell and rubs against the oyster's body. The mantle covers the object with thin layers of shell material, and in this way forms a pearl. Pearls used as gems come from pearl oysters. Pearls produced by the oysters used as food have little value.

An oyster has many enemies, such as fish, sea stars, crabs, and snails. Human beings are probably the oyster's greatest enemy. More oysters are caught and eaten than any other shellfish. *See also* PEARL. J.J.A./C.S.H.

OZONE (ō′ zōn′) Ozone (O_3) is a dark blue gas. It boils at $-111°C$ [$-168°F$] and freezes at $-192°C$ [$-314°F$]. Ozone is an allotrope of oxygen. (*See* ALLOTROPE.) This means that its molecules contain only oxygen atoms, but their number and arrangement are different from oxygen. Normal oxygen has two atoms of oxygen in each molecule. Ozone has three atoms of oxygen to each molecule. The atoms in a molecule of ozone are arranged in a triangle.

Ozone is formed when electricity is passed through air or pure oxygen. The smell of electric motors is due to ozone. The ozone is produced by sparking in the motor. A thin layer of ozone forms in the upper atmosphere by the action of sunlight on oxygen. Ozone in the upper atmosphere protects human life by screening out the harmful ultraviolet rays in sunlight. But in the lower atmosphere, ozone is a harmful pollutant, formed when nitrogen oxides in automobile exhaust react with the oxygen in the air. Ozone belongs to a class of air pollutants called petrochemical oxidants. (*See* POLLUTION.) Because it is a powerful oxidizing agent, ozone is used to sterilize water and decolorize foods, and as a bleach. (*See* OXIDATION AND REDUCTION.)   M.E./J.R.W.

PACK RAT (pak rat) The pack rat, sometimes called a "wood rat," is a blunt-faced rodent found in North and Central America. The animal has brownish gray fur and, unlike many rats, a hairy tail.

Western pack rats often live in mountains, building nests on rock ledges. Others live in growths such as cactuses. A female has one or two litters a season. Each litter consists of three to six young.

The pack rat gets its name from picking up and hiding small articles it finds attractive. Among such items could be silverware, nails, and brightly colored stones. The animal is also known as a "trade rat." This is because it often discards an item it is carrying in favor of picking up something else.   J.J.A./J.J.M.

PADDLEFISH (pad′ əl fish′) A paddlefish is a primitive freshwater fish that belongs to the family Polyodontidae. It can grow to 1.8 m [6 ft] in length and more than 45 kg [99 lb] in weight. The paddlefish gets its name because it has a long projection on its snout. The projection is shaped like a canoe paddle. It is not known what the paddle-shaped snout is used for. Some ichthyologists (scientists who study fish) think that the paddlefish may use it to stir up the bottom of a river to find food. The paddlefish is omnivorous, eating plankton and other small organisms. (*See* ICHTHYOLOGY; OMNIVORE; PLANKTON.)

Paddlefish were once common in the Missouri River. Their numbers have been decreased due to the building of dams and heavy fishing. The flesh of the fish is often eaten smoked. The eggs are made into caviar. Recently, paddlefish from the Missouri River were transferred to rivers in Tennessee where their numbers are now increasing. Another species of paddlefish is found in China.

S.R.G./E.C.M.

PAGODA TREE (pə gōd′ ə) A pagoda tree is any of several species of trees that are pyramid-shaped, or shaped like a pagoda. They are all members of the pea family. The Japanese pagoda tree (*Sophora japonica*) grows in China and Korea. It reaches a height of 22 m [75 ft]. It has alternate leaves, each of which is made up of about 15 leaflets. (*See* LEAF.) White flowers hang in long clusters and produce fruits called pods. *See also* PEA FAMILY.   A.J.C./M.H.S.

PAIN (pān) Pain is an unpleasant sensation that is usually caused by an injury, disease, or other disorder. It is important because, though disagreeable, it warns the body that something is wrong.

The sensation of pain is received by special nerve endings called pain receptors.

These pain receptors are located throughout the body as well as in the skin. The receptors are connected to chains of nerve cells. To carry a pain impulse to the brain, each nerve cell releases a chemical called a neurotransmitter. (*See* NERVE CELL.)

Superficial pain is caused by receptors in the skin. A person can usually tell the exact location of superficial pain because the skin has so many pain receptors. Deep pain—pain from the internal organs—is harder to pinpoint because there are fewer deep pain receptors. Sometimes deep pain may be referred. Referred pain is felt in a part of the body that is some distance from the actual source of the pain. Referred pain is common in toothaches.

Pain can best be overcome by treating the cause. Pain can be controlled by certain drugs, such as aspirin. Narcotics are usually used only for very severe pain. (*See* NARCOTIC.) For chronic (long-term) pain, a surgeon may destroy part of the brain or spinal cord in order to interrupt the pain pathway. *See also* NERVOUS SYSTEM.   A.J.C./J.J.F.

PAINT (pānt) Paint is a mixture of one or more colored powders and a liquid. The colored powder is called a pigment. The liquid is called a vehicle or binder. The vehicle carries the pigment and allows it to be spread. Many vehicles contain a solvent or thinner.

There are basically two types of pigments—prime and inert. Prime pigments give paint its color. Inert pigments are materials such as calcium carbonate, clay, mica, or talc. Such substances make paint last longer.

Vehicles include oils, varnishes, latex, and various types of resins. When a vehicle comes in contact with air, it dries and hardens. This activity causes paint to become a hard film. This film holds the pigment on a surface.

Solvents or thinners are added to paint to make it more liquid. For example, latex paints are thinned with water. These paints are therefore called water-thinned paints.

Types of paints There are various types of paints that are commonly used. Oil-based paints are often used as outside paints, and on walls and floors. Such paints often protect wood and metal. Latex paints include wall paints, masonry paints, and outside paints. Latex paints are often preferred over oil-based paints. Latex paints are easier to use. Also, the painting equipment (such as brushes) can be easily cleaned using soap and water. Many masonry paints are made with polyvinyl acetate or acrylic emulsions. (*See* EMULSION.) Lacquers are often used to cover automobiles. A lacquer is made up of a solution of resins in a solvent. The solvent dries up after the lacquer is put on. (*See* RESIN.) Fire-retardant paints protect against fire damage. But no paint is completely fireproof. Good fire-retardant paint contains nitrogen chemicals. These chemicals make the paint puff up when it is near fire. The blister forms a barrier between the flame and the surface. Heat-resisting paints are used to cover warm and hot surfaces. Alkyd resin or silicon resin vehicles are often used for surfaces such as those on engines or ovens. Cement water paints add color to cement surfaces, such as a basement floor. Metallic paints are made with aluminum or bronze powder. They have many uses, such as on bridges. Wood and plaster primers are used for first coats on plaster and wood walls. These paints fill the tiny openings in the wood and plaster. This allows other paints to stick to the surface but not sink into it. Enamels contain small amounts of prime pigments. The low pigment content makes the paint dry with a high gloss. Enamels are often used in bathrooms and kitchens.

Manufacture of paints The first step is mixing. A small amount of the vehicle is put into a large mechanical mixer at the paint factory. Powdered pigment is slowly added to the vehicle, making a heavy paste. The next step is grinding. A worker puts the paste into a mill, or grinder, to break up the pigment par-

Modern pigments allow a very wide range of colors and shades. These samples of paint are some of the many different colors that can be produced.

ticles and scatter them throughout the vehicle. This operation is followed by thinning and drying. Another worker pours the ground paste into a tank, where it is mechanically mixed with more vehicle, solvents, and driers. The paint is mixed until it is nearly thin enough for use. Tinting is the next process. A tinter adds a small amount of pigment to give the paint the exact color and shade desired. The final steps include straining and packaging. The paint is strained through a type of filter to remove any solid bits of dust or dirt. The paint is then poured into a filling tank, and finally into the metal cans in which it is sold.

Application of paints Paints are usually put on in several layers or coats, one on top of another. The first coat, or primer, prepares the surface for the rest of the paint. The second coat, or undercoat, is heavily charged with pigment and is matt (not glossy or shiny). The finishing coat is sometimes glossy. The way in which the paint is put on depends on the type of job. Brushes, rollers, or sprays may be used, or the article may be dipped or tumbled in paint. Decorative paints dry in the air but industrial paints are often heat-dried. This process, called stoving, speeds production and gives tough paint surfaces.

More and new types of paints are being produced. Research projects conducted by chemists and engineers have become a major part of paint manufacturing. The amount of paint sold in the United States in one year would cover more than 32,000 sq km [12,000 sq mi].   J.J.A./R.W.L.

A worker is shown spraying paint on an automobile body. Industrial paints provide hard, corrosion-resistant and colorful surfaces to a wide range of manufacturers. Lacquer paints are often used to cover automobiles. A lacquer is made up of a solution of resins in a solvent. The solvent dries up after the lacquer is put on.

PALEOBOTANY (pā′ lē ō bät′ ən ē)
Paleobotany is the study of fossil plants. Most plants do not have hard parts that can be preserved in rocks. Sometimes, impressions of plants are found embedded in clay. More often, however, plant remnants are found petrified. A plant becomes petrified when its decaying cells are replaced by silica or calcium carbonate. The result is an exact duplicate of the original plant.

The history of plant life on earth has been traced by paleobotanists. Primitive algae existed during Precambrian times. Psilophytes, the first land plants, existed during the early Devonian period. During the Pennsylvanian period, huge forests of club mosses, ferns, and horsetails grew. These forests died and decayed, and the remaining organic matter was changed into coal. (*See* COAL.) Gymnosperms thrived during the Mesozoic era. In the late Mesozoic era, flowering plants appeared. Flowering plants are still the dominant land plants on earth. *See also* PALEONTOLOGY; EVOLUTION; FOSSIL.

J.M.C./W.R.S.

PALEOCENE EPOCH (pā′ lē ə sēn′ ep′ ək) The Paleocene epoch is the earliest subdivision of the Tertiary period. It began about 65 million years ago and lasted about 11 million years.

A worldwide warming trend occurred during the Paleocene epoch. The dinosaurs and other giant reptiles of the Mesozoic era had become extinct. Mammals became more widespread and diversified. Primates, small reptiles, amphibians, and fish were abundant. Flowering plants flourished during the Paleocene epoch. Deposits of gas, oil, and coal formed.

There is evidence suggesting that North America and western Europe were part of one continent during the Paleocene epoch. *See also* CONTINENTAL DRIFT; GEOLOGICAL TIME SCALE; TERTIARY PERIOD.

J.M.C./W.R.S.

PALEOCLIMATOLOGY (pā′ lē ō klī′ mə täl′ ə jē) Paleoclimatology is the study of ancient climates. Paleoclimatologists try to determine and explain the types of climate that have existed on earth since the earliest geological ages. Since most evidence of paleoclimates is found indirectly through rocks and fossils, the paleoclimatologist has a difficult job. There are, however, several indications of paleoclimates that many scientists consider reliable.

Hot paleoclimates are often indicated by limestone formations, coral reefs, and fossils of dinosaurs and tropical plants. Cold paleoclimates are indicated by evidence of glaciation (coverings of ice). This evidence includes masses of rocks and boulders, moraines, fjords, and drumlins. Fossils of conifers are another good indication of a cold paleoclimate.

Arid (dry) paleoclimates are indicated by large salt deposits. Other evidence includes well-preserved animal footprints and plants with small, pale leaves. Humid paleoclimates are indicated by dry lake beds, coal deposits, peat bogs, and fossils of tree ferns.

Many scientists believe that the warm climates of the past occurred because the continents lay close to the equator. Eventually, the continents drifted to their present positions. (*See* CONTINENTAL DRIFT.) Some scientists suggest that the sun's radiation has varied because of sunspot activity.

During the last 600,000 years, there have been at least four ice ages. Paleoclimatologists still can not explain why these periods of glaciation occurred. *See also* FOSSIL; GEOLOGICAL TIME SCALE; GLACIATION; PALEOBOTANY. J.M.C./W.R.S.

PALEONTOLOGY (pā′ lē än′ täl′ ə jē) Paleontology is the study of the fossil remnants of plants and animals. The study of fossil plants is sometimes considered a separate field called paleobotany. (*See* PALEOBOTANY.)

Fossils are found in layers of sedimentary rock. (*See* SEDIMENTARY ROCK.) Through complex methods of dating, paleontologists can find out the age of the fossils, and thus the age of the rock in which the fossils are found. Paleontologists can also find out whether the rock was formed on land or underwater. Fossils give a good indication of the evolutionary process. (*See* EVOLUTION.) Paleontology is also used in prospecting and geology. *See also* DATING; FOSSIL.   J.M.C./W.R.S.

PALEOZOIC ERA (pā′ lē ə zō′ ik ir ə) The Paleozoic era began about 570 million years ago and lasted about 345 million years. It includes seven geological periods: Cambrian, Ordovician, Silurian, Devonian, Mississippian, Pennsylvanian, and Permian. The Mississippian and Pennsylvanian periods are often combined to form the Carboniferous period.

The early Paleozoic era is characterized by algae, trilobites, and other primitive forms of water life. The first fish probably evolved during the Cambrian period. Much of North America was covered by water during the Cambrian and Ordovician periods.

The middle Paleozoic era is characterized by the rapid development of fish and the evolution of amphibians. The first air-breathing animals appeared during the Silurian period. Sharks and armored fish developed. The first forests grew in the swamps of the Devonian period. Shelled animals and amphibians were abundant by the Mississippian period. Limestone, coal, oil, and deposits of iron ore, zinc, and lead formed.

The middle Paleozoic era is characterized by the rapid development of fish and the evolution of amphibians. In the warm climate of the Devonian period (about 398-345 million years ago) of the Paleozoic era, the first forests began growing in the swamps, rivers and lakes dried up, and many fish died. The lobe-finned fish (below), however, could breathe air and move about on land on their muscular fins. These fish probably evolved into early amphibians.

The last two periods of the Paleozoic era are characterized by the development of reptiles and conifers. Some of the primitive organisms of the Cambrian period became extinct. Fish, amphibians, and reptiles were all plentiful by the end of the Permian period. The Ural and Appalachian Mountains formed during this time. Large coal deposits also formed during the Pennsylvanian period. *See also* EVOLUTION; GEOLOGICAL TIME SCALE.

J.M.C./W.R.S.

PALLADIUM (pə lād′ ē əm) Palladium (Pd) is a rare and valuable silvery metallic element. Its atomic number is 46 and its atomic weight is 106.4. It melts at 1,552°C [2,827°F] and boils at 3,140°C [5,684°F]. Its relative density is 12.0.

Palladium was discovered in 1804 by a British chemist William Wollaston. It is found in platinum ores and is very similar to platinum in its properties. Palladium is used to make alloys, especially with gold and silver. These alloys are used in jewelry and for fillings in dentistry. Most palladium is used in industry as a catalyst for reacting hydrogen. (*See* CATALYST.) Palladium is used because it can absorb 900 times its own volume of hydrogen. M.E./J.R.W.

PALM FAMILY The palm (pälm) family includes over 1000 species of plants in the tropic and sub-tropic regions of the world. Although many are low-lying plants with spiral-growing leaves, the best-known species are the palm trees. They can grow 33.3 m [110 ft] tall. The trunk of the palm tree is hard on the outside, but soft in the center. The leaves often grow as long as 12.1 m [40 ft]. Palm trees produce many valuable items. Timber is cut from the trunk. Mats, clothes, and roofs are made from the trunk and leaves. The sap is made into drinks. The fruits of the trees are often delicious. Coconuts and dates are both fruits from palm trees. S.R.G./M.H.S.

The many species of palm trees which grow in tropic and sub-tropic regions provide useful and valuable products including oil, fiber, timber, coconuts, dates, and sap.

PANCREAS (pang′ krē əs) The pancreas is an important organ found in the bodies of human beings and in all animals with backbones. It produces a strong digestive juice that breaks down food in the intestines and produces the hormones insulin and glucagon.

The human pancreas is a pinkish yellow gland about 15 to 20 cm [6 to 8 in] long, 3.8 cm [1.5 in] wide, and 2.5 cm [1 in] thick. It lies crossways behind the stomach.

Digestive juices from the pancreas flow into the small intestine, or duodenum. The juices contain enzymes and salts that help digest proteins, starches, sugars, and fats.

Small fragments of tissue, called islets of Langerhans, are scattered throughout the pancreas. They secrete (give off) insulin directly into the blood stream, which carries it to cells throughout the body. The cells need insulin to help them use glucose, the sugar that is their main fuel. The islets of Langerhans also secrete glucagon into the blood. Glucagon acts on the liver, causing it to release stored glucose into the blood. *See also* BANTING, SIR FREDERICK; DIABETES; DIGESTION; INSULIN. W.R.P./J.J.F.

PANDA (pan′ də) A panda is one of two species of omnivorous mammals native to China and eastern Asia. Both of these species

The lesser panda (above), or red panda, lives in the mountains of eastern Asia and spends most of the day asleep in trees.

The giant panda (above), a very rare animal, lives in the bamboo forests of western China. It may eat more than 9 kg [20 lb] of food each day.

have an "extra thumb" on the wrist of the forepaws. This thumb helps the panda hold things in its paws.

The giant panda (*Ailuropoda melano-leuca*) has a white, bearlike body with black hair on its ears, shoulders, arms, legs, and around the eyes. It reaches a body length of 1.5 m [5 ft] and a weight of 160 kg [350 lb]. The giant panda feeds mostly on bamboo and plants, but sometimes eats fish and other small animals. A giant panda may eat more than 9 kg [20 lb] of food each day. It lives on the ground and stays alone except during mating season. The giant panda is very rare and is protected by law in China. Though some taxonomists classify the giant panda as a member of the raccoon family, most classify it as a bear and others classify it in a totally separate family. (*See* RACCOON.)

The lesser panda (*Ailurus fulgens*) is also called the red panda or cat-bear. It is much smaller than the giant panda. Its body is about 60 cm [24 in] long, and its bushy, ringed tail is about 50 cm [20 in] long. It weighs about 4 kg [8.8 lb]. Its fur is reddish brown on the back and black on the belly. Its face has white

markings. The lesser panda lives in the mountains of eastern Asia and spends most of the day asleep in the trees. Lesser pandas usually stay in groups of two or more. The lesser panda is classified as a member of the raccoon family. *See also* CLASSIFICATION OF LIVING ORGANISMS; MAMMAL. A.J.C./J.J.M.

PANGOLIN (pang′ gə lan) The pangolin, or scaly anteater, is a mammal that belongs to the scaly anteater family, Manidae. Pangolins look like the anteater and the armadillo. They vary in length from 0.9 to 1.5 m [3 to 5 ft], and have overlapping, horny, brown scales that resemble coats of mail worn by medieval knights. Pangolins are toothless. They have narrow snouts, long tails, and sticky, ropelike tongues. They can thrust their tongues far out to catch the ants on which they feed.

Pangolins live in southeastern Asia, Indonesia, and parts of Africa north of the Sahara. Pangolins roll themselves into a tight ball when attacked. They are so heavily armored that few enemies can harm them.

Pangolins are hunted for their excellent meat. However, because they are shy and only look for food at night, they are hard to find. *See also* ANTEATER.   W.R.P./J.J.M.

A pangolin, or scaly anteater, is shown above.

PANTOGRAPH (pant′ ə graf′) A pantograph is an instrument used by artists and draftsmen. It is used for copying a design or plan onto a sheet of paper. A pantograph is made up of a number of rods. These rods are joined together by pins that can be adjusted. A pointer is moved over the lines of the design or plan. This movement is transferred by the rods to a pencil or pen at the other end. This traces out a copy of the original drawing. The size of the copy can be altered by adjusting the position of the rods.   M.E./R.W.L.

PAPER

Paper (pā′ pər) is one of the most useful materials in any civilization. The product is involved in nearly every aspect of people's everyday lives. Books, magazines, and newspapers are printed on paper. Education, government, and industry could not operate without it.

The world's first maker of paper was the wasp. The wasp chews tiny pieces of wood until they form a pulp. The wasp then spits out the wet pulp and smooths it into a thin sheet. When the pulp dries, it becomes paper. It is used by certain kinds of wasps to build their homes. (*See* WASP.)

Thousands of years ago, people wrote on strips of bark from trees, on silk, and on skins of sheep or goats. Animal skins prepared for writing were called parchment.

Paper gets its name from papyrus, a sheet made by pressing together the core material (pith) of the Egyptian papyrus plant. Papyrus as a writing material was first developed about 6,000 years ago in Egypt. It was not until about 2,000 years later that paper, as it is known today, was invented in China.

All paper is formed into sheets from cellulose fibers. Cellulose is a substance found in most plants. (*See* CELLULOSE.) Various types of trees, cotton plants, rice and wheat straws, cornstalks, hemp, and jute are plants especially used for papermaking.

Most of the paper produced in the United States comes from wood pulp. This pulp is obtained from trees and waste materials of lumbering operations. Some paper is made from pulp recycled from waste paper.

There are thousands of kinds of paper. The type of finished paper depends totally on the manufacturing and chemical processes that it has passed through.

How paper is made   For many years, rags were the main raw material for paper. Today, they have been largely replaced by wood pulp. Wood pulp comes from softwood trees such as pine, spruce, and hemlock. Most pulpwood is made by the mechanical, or ground-wood, process and by chemical processes.

1.

2.

4.

3.

Stages in the manufacture of paper are shown. 1. Logs from softwood trees are debarked in a large revolving drum. 2. The debarked logs are fed into a grinder to make pulp. 3. After being dried and pressed, the pulp is shipped to a paper mill, where it is mixed with water in a hydrapulper. 4. After further preparation, the woodpulp mixture is fed into the "wet end" of a papermaking machine. 5. A huge roll of paper emerges from the "dry end" of the machine.

5.

The mechanical process is used mainly for the production of cheap papers, such as paper on which newspapers are printed. In this process, the debarked logs are pressed against a revolving grindstone. Water is sprayed against the grindstone to prevent it from getting too hot.

The chief chemical processes for making pulp from wood are the sulfite, sulfate, and soda processes. In all of these processes, the wood is thoroughly washed with water and cut into chips. In the sulfite process, the wood chips are cooked in a digester, which is a closed tank. The chips cook in a solution of calcium bisulfide under steam pressure until the wood forms a pulp. In the sulfate process, the wood is cooked in a solution of caustic soda and sodium sulfide. In the soda process, the wood chips are cooked with caustic soda solution to dissolve the materials which hold the cellulose, or papermaking fibers.

The mechanical or chemical pulp produced by the above processes is screened, washed, and bleached, and then dried and pressed into sheets.

Most paper is made on the Fourdrinier machine. It consists of a belt of wire mesh on which watery pulp is spread. The belt passes through a series of rollers, which press the water out of the pulp. The belt then passes under a turning cylinder called a dandy roll. The dandy roll gives the paper a woven or flat surface. Near the end of the machine, the belt passes through two felt-covered couching rolls, which press out more water. It then goes through two sets of smooth metal press rolls. The press rolls give the paper a smooth finish. The last step before cutting is calendering, or pressing the paper between chilled rollers. Calendering gives the paper an even smoother finish, called a machine finish. At the end of the Fourdrinier machine, the paper is wound on spools into large rolls. The paper is slit into strips and cut into sheets.

"Water marking," for good quality writing paper, is done by pressing a design into the moist paper at the "wet end" of the machine. Tissue paper is made in the same way as ordinary paper except that it is scraped by a knife edge as it leaves the drying rollers, giving a tissuey finish.

Paper recycling Paper recycling is the use of waste paper to make new paper. Such discarded items as grocery bags and newspapers are collected, cleaned, and made into pulp. The pulp can be used in making such products as newsprint, paper board, tissue, and writing paper. During the 1960s, a growing concern about pollution promoted greater recycling efforts to reduce solid wastes. During the mid-1970s, the need for recycling larger quantities of waste paper became apparent during a paper shortage. This shortage occurred because the paper industry could no longer meet the rapidly growing demand for paper.

Chemical engineers have found many ways of treating paper to make it strong, fireproof, and resistant to liquids and acids. As a result, paper can, in many instances, replace cloth, metal, and wood. For example, specially treated paper is used to make clothing, such as surgical gowns and disposable diapers.

Paper consumption per person is often considered a reliable index to the standard of living. In other words, the higher the standard of living and the greater the national wealth, the greater the amount of paper used. The United States uses about 280 kg [620 lb] of paper and paperboard per person every year.

J.J.A./F.W.S.

PARACHUTE (par′ ə shüt′) A parachute looks similar to a large umbrella, but is made of a light fabric. It is used to slow down the fall of a person or object from an airplane or any other great height.

A parachute operates on simple principles. There are two forces that act upon any

The parachutist (above) is shown during a parachute drop from an airplane.

This jet aircraft (below) uses a parachute as an extra brake to slow its landing speed.

falling object—air resistance and gravity. Gravity pulls the object quickly toward the earth. But air resists the object's movement. At low speeds, the pull of gravity is much stronger than the resistance of air. Thus, air resistance has little effect. But, air resistance becomes larger as the speed of fall increases. Eventually, the object reaches speed called terminal velocity where air resistance and the pull of gravity just balance. From that point on, the object falls with constant speed. Large, flat surfaces offer a greater area of resistance than do thin, sharp surfaces. Therefore, an object shaped like a saucer reaches its terminal velocity sooner, so it falls much more slowly than one shaped like a needle.

Parachutes designed for human use are made of nylon. In the early years of aviation, parachutes where made of silk. The average parachute is about 7 to 9 m [24 to 28 ft] across when open. Parachutes for cargo may be as large as 30 m [100 ft] across.

Parachutes are worn on a harness which consists of a series of straps fitted around the shoulders and legs of the parachutist. The parachute is tightly packed into a compact bundle with a canvas cover. It is worn either as a seat pack (to be sat on) or as a chest or back pack.

Special straps, called risers, are attached to the shoulder portion of the harness. They hold the lines, or shrouds, which are attached to the canopy, the umbrellalike part of the parachute. A ring for pulling the rip cord is attached to one of the straps. The rip cord opens the parachute pack. When it is pulled, the parachute springs out of its tight confinement, and the air forces it open. Sometimes a special line, called a static line, is used to open a parachute. The static line is attached to the airplane. When the parachutist jumps from the airplane, the static line pulls open the parachute automatically, and then releases itself. The static line is usually used in military aircraft that carry large amounts of paratroopers (soldiers).

As soon as the parachute canopy opens completely, the air slows the descent of the parachutist so quickly that he is jerked sharply. Parachutes with holes, or slots, in their canopies have been developed to reduce the force of this opening shock.

Parachutists descend at the rate of about 5 m [15 ft] per second, or slightly faster. Parachute drops from less than 150 m [500 ft] above the ground are dangerous because this height does not allow the parachute time to open. Parachutists can control the direction of their descent by pulling on the shrouds. Parachutists often land with great force. Heavy boots and special shock-absorbing techniques help prevent sprained ankles and broken legs. Experienced parachutists can often land very lightly in a standing position.

Parachute jumping has become a popular sport in the United States and Europe. There are many clubs and national and international jumping events in which parachutists try to land on small targets on the ground.

W.R.P./R.W.L.

PARAFFIN (par′ ə fən) Paraffin is a white, waxy, solid hydrocarbon mixture that has no taste nor odor. It is partly clear and is used to put a waterproof coating on cardboard containers such as milk cartons. Paraffin is also the main ingredient in candles.

Paraffins are made from a mixture of high-boiling petroleum fractions, which are products separated from petroleum. The fractions are chilled and pressed through a filter to remove heavy oil. The remaining solid is paraffin wax.

Ordinary paraffin wax melts at 32 to 66°C [90 to 150°F]. Microcrystalline paraffin wax is another type of paraffin wax. It melts at 66 to 85°C [150 to 185°F].

Paraffin wax is also used in certain kinds of polishes and as a moisture-proof coating on textiles. Jars for preserving food are often sealed with paraffin wax. *See also* HYDRO-CARBON; PETROLEUM.

W.R.P./J.M.

PARAKEET (par′ ə kēt′) A parakeet is a bird that belongs to the parrot family Psittacidae. A parakeet is a small parrot with a long tail. (*See* PARROT.) There are several species in the world. Most live in Australia, India, or Africa. Parakeets eat flowers, fruits, and seeds. They are very colorful and often kept as pets. The Carolina parakeet, once found in the United States, is now extinct.

S.R.G./L.L.S.

PARALLAX (par′ ə laks′) Suppose that you are looking at an object against a background. As you move your head, the object seems to move against the background. This effect is called parallax. In astronomy parallax is used to find the distances of the planets and the nearer stars. The position of a planet is measured. Then it is measured 12 hours later. In this time the measuring instrument has moved in space because of the earth's rotation. Because of this the planet seems to move against the background of stars. The amount that it moves depends on its distance. Therefore its distance can be worked out. This method is also used for measuring the distances to nearby stars. In this case the positions of a star are measured six months apart. In this time the earth has moved around to the opposite side of the sun. This large movement of the earth produces a small apparent movement in the star. Therefore its distance can be measured.

Parallax is also important when you are reading the dial on a scientific instrument. The pointer on the dial is always a small distance away from the scale. If you read the dial at an angle, the pointer gives a wrong reading because of parallax. This is overcome by having a mirror on the scale. The pointer is lined up with its reflection. Then you are directly above the pointer and the reading is accurate.

M.E./S.S.B.

PARALYSIS (pə ral′ ə səs) Paralysis is the loss of use of muscles. Sometimes a whole group of muscles becomes completely useless and paralyzed. Sometimes there is only partial paralysis. Paralysis itself is not a disease. It is caused by disease or damage to the brain or the nerves that stimulate the muscles. For instance, if a person has a badly damaged spinal cord, there will be paralysis of all the muscles below the injury. If the nerves that carry messages back to the brain are also affected, there will be no feeling in the lower half of the body.

Doctors divide paralysis into two main types. In spastic paralysis, the muscles affected are tense, as though they were pulling, but are weak and cannot be controlled. Spastic paralysis is usually due to damage in the brain or the upper part of the spinal cord. In flaccid paralysis, the muscles are limp and flabby. Flaccid paralysis is due to damage to nerves lower down in the nervous system. Poliomyelitis causes this type of paralysis.

When paralysis continues for a long time, the nerves and the muscles become permanently useless. The nerve cells die, and the muscles become thin and wasted. To prevent this, electrical treatment can be given by physical therapists to keep the muscles active. The electrical impulse makes the muscles contract, even though the patient is unable to control them himself.

D.M.H.W./J.J.F.

PARAMECIUM (par′ ə mē′ shəm) The paramecium is a one-celled animal that lives in fresh water. (*See* PROTOZOA.) Because of its slipperlike shape, it is sometimes called a slipper animalcule. Its body is covered with tiny, hairlike cilia which it uses for movement and for feeding. (*See* CILIUM.) On one side is an oral groove which leads to the mouth and gullet. Cilia on this groove create a flow of algae, bacteria, and other tiny organisms into the mouth. Food is digested in food vacuoles which form at the end of the gullet. (*See* VACUOLE.) Wastes from digestion are ejected through an anal pore. There are two or three contractile vacuoles located near the surface at the ends of the paramecium. These contractile vacuoles regulate the amount of water inside the paramecium and get rid of metabolic wastes by squirting the water and wastes out of the cell. (*See* METABOLISM.)

The body of the paramecium has an outer membrane called a pellicle. Just inside the pellicle is a layer of firm, clear cytoplasm called ectoplasm. The watery cytoplasm with its various structures is called endoplasm.

The paramecium has one large nucleus—macronucleus—and one or more smaller nuclei—micronuclei. The macronucleus controls most of the cell's activities and contains genes. The micronucleus also contains genes and functions in sexual reproduction. Paramecia usually reproduce asexually by dividing into two new organisms. (*See* ASEXUAL REPRODUCTION.) Occasionally, paramecia reproduce sexually in a process called conjugation. Two paramecia line up next to each other and form a tubelike structure between them. They exchange micronuclei, separate, and divide several times. Conjugation has a revitalizing effect on paramecia. Without conjugation, a paramecium grows old and dies. *See also* CELL.

A.J.C./C.S.H.

The paramecium (above) is a tiny one-celled organism found in fresh water.

PARASITE (par′ ə sīt′) A parasite is a plant or animal that lives with or inside another living organism—the host—in order to feed or find shelter. Some parasites eat the flesh of the host. Others eat the food that the host has eaten. Other parasites just live in or on the host for safety. Parasites always harm the host although they rarely kill it. If they did kill the host, the parasites would destroy their home and source for food. Parasites often weaken the host to the point where it may die of other causes, such as disease. Some parasites have parasites—smaller organisms called hyperparasites—within them.

Animal parasites Nearly every animal on earth has parasites. The average human being has several parasites in his or her body. Nearly every major phylum of animals on earth includes species which are parasitic. Most of the animal parasites belong to the phyla Protozoa, Platyhelminthes, Aschelminthes, and Arthropoda. (*See* ARTHROPODA; ASCHELMINTHES; PLATYHELMINTHES; PROTOZOA.)

Ectoparasites live on the outside of their hosts. One well-known ectoparasite is the flea. (*See* FLEA.) The flea is an insect that lives in the fur and feathers of animals. It feeds by sticking its sharp ''beak'' into the animals' skin and sucking out blood. Besides causing an irritation to the host, fleas can also spread serious diseases. Plague is a disease caused by bacteria spread by fleas that live on rats. In the 1300s, an epidemic of plague called the Black Death killed millions of Europeans. (*See* EPIDEMIC.)

Other well-known ectoparasites include ticks, leeches, and mosquitoes. (*See* LEECH; MOSQUITO; TICK.) Unlike fleas, leeches, and ticks, mosquitoes do not spend all their time on the host. They land on the skin, puncture the skin with their beak, suck out some of the hosts' blood, and leave. Mosquitoes often spread disease and endoparasites between hosts.

Endoparasites are parasites which live and feed inside the bodies of their hosts. They feed on blood, tissue, tissue fluids, and the food of the hosts. Endoparasites are responsible for some of the world's most serious diseases, such as malaria, sleeping sickness, and bilharzia. (*See* MALARIA.) Malaria and sleeping sickness are caused by microscopic, one-

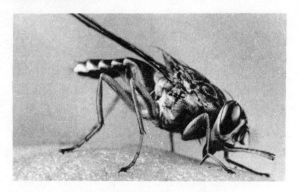

Trypanosomes, parasites which cause sleeping sickness, have two hosts—the tsetse fly and a vertebrate. A tsetse fly (above) spreads parasites by drinking blood from an infected person or animal.

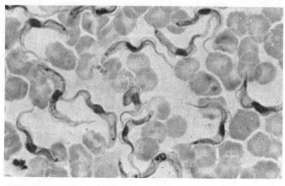

Sleeping sickness trypanosomes are shown in blood, magnified 500 times. Parasites invade the fluid surrounding the brain and spinal cord, causing loss of consciousness and, frequently, death.

celled animals that live in the bloodstream of mammals. They are spread by biting insects.

Many endoparasites are worms. Tapeworms live in the throat, stomach, or intestines of their host. They attach themselves to the host by means of a sucker. The worms absorb into their skin part of the food that the host swallows. Eggs of the tapeworms pass through the hosts' bodies in the feces.

Another parasitic worm—the blood fluke—lives in the blood of its host. When large numbers of flukes collect in the blood vessels, serious injury and even death may occur. The condition caused by this fluke is called bilharzia. (*See* BILHARZIA.)

Social parasites Parasites that affect a group of organisms—rather than just one organism—are called social parasites. The best-known social parasites are the cuckoo birds of Europe, Asia, and Africa. (*See* CUCKOO.) These birds lay their eggs in the nests of other birds. The host birds raise and feed the young cuckoos. In this way, the entire population of birds is affected. Some bees and wasps are social parasites, too.

Parasitic plants The reason that there are fewer plant parasites is that most plants are able to produce their own food by photosynthesis. (*See* PHOTOSYNTHESIS.) Therefore, they do not need to parasitize other or-

ganisms. Some plants cannot make their own food and have become parasites. The dodder is a simple plant that resembles pink cotton. It winds itself around other plants, sends suckers into the other plants, and absorbs food. Mistletoe can produce food by photosynthesis, but it must get its water and minerals from trees.   S.R.G./C.R.N.

This photomicrograph shows a dodder stem (lengthwise section) with its suckers in the host stem (cross section). The dodder is a parasitic plant which twines around the stem of its host and absorbs food by sinking suckers, or haustoria, into the host's cambium (living tissue).

PARENCHYMA (pə reng′ kə mə) Parenchyma is living plant tissue that is made up of thin-walled, 14-sided cells. The cells are not specialized, but will soon undergo differentiation. (*See* DIFFERENTIATION, CELLULAR.) Parenchyma cells may be either loosely or densely packed.

Leaf parenchyma cells contain chlorophyll and make up the tissues in which most of the photosynthesis takes place. (*See* LEAF.) The cortex (outer part) and pith (inner part) of stems and roots is parenchyma. (*See*

CORTEX.) The soft, fleshy tissues of fruits are also made of parenchyma. (*See* FRUIT.) Collenchyma and schlerenchyma develop from parenchyma. *See also* COLLENCHYMA; SCHLERENCHYMA. A.J.C./M.H.S.

PARROT (par′ ət) A parrot is a bird that belongs to the family Psittacidae. It is a stout bird with a heavy bill and strong talons. Most parrots are very colorful. They live in the forests of the tropical and sub-tropical regions. There are over 300 species. They eat seeds, nuts, buds, fruit, and nectar.

Parrots are commonly kept as pets. They may be taught how to talk, for they can easily imitate various sounds. *See also* COCKATOO; PARAKEET. S.R.G./L.L.S.

The parrot family includes more than 300 species of birds. They are popular pets because of their bright colors and ability to imitate sounds.

PARSEC (pär′ sek′) A parsec is the distance to a star whose position seems to shift by 1 second of arc when viewed from opposite sides of the earth's orbit. (*See* PARALLAX.) It is equal to 3.26 light-years, or 30.9 trillion km [19.2 trillion mi]. The term parsec comes from the words parallax and second.

Parsecs are used to measure distances in the universe. Proxima Centauri, the nearest star to the sun, is about 1.3 parsecs away. The sun is about 8,000 parsecs from the center of the galaxy. *See also* LIGHT-YEAR.
J.M.C./C.R.

PARSLEY FAMILY The parsley (pär′ slē) family includes about 1,500 species of herbaceous plants, most of which live in northern temperate regions. They have dark green, compound leaves growing in clusters around the hollow stem. (*See* LEAF.) The flowers are usually greenish white and grow in umbels on the stem. (*See* INFLORESCENCE.)

The parsley plant (*Petroselinum sativum*) is a biennial plant native to the Mediterranean area. Its leaves are used fresh or dried as a garnish or flavoring for food. It is a good source of iron and vitamins A and C. Other members of this family include the carrot, celery, hemlock, and parsnip. This family is sometimes called the carrot family.
A.J.C./M.H.S.

PARSNIP (pär′ snəp) Parsnip (*Pastinaca sativa*) is a biennial herbaceous plant belonging to the parsley family. It has lobed leaves and yellow flowers. Parsnip is cultivated for its large, white, carrot-shaped tap root. (*See* ROOT.) The root is harvested after the first growing season and is usually served as a cooked vegetable. It is rich in carbohydrates and vitamins A and C. *See also* PARSLEY FAMILY. A.J.C./F.W.S.

PARTHENOCARP (pär′ thə nō kärp′) A parthenocarp is a seedless fruit that develops without pollination. (*See* POLLINATION.) Bananas and pineapples are common parthenocarps. Some parthenocarps, such as seedless tomatoes, can be artificially formed by using a special hormone that prevents the pollination of flowers. *See also* FRUIT.
A.J.C./M.H.S.

PARTHENOGENESIS (pär′ thə nō jen′ə səs) Parthenogenesis is a type of asexual reproduction in which an unfertilized egg develops into a mature organism. It is common along lower plants and some invertebrate animals, such as rotifers and insects. (*See* INSECT; ROTIFER.) Male ants, bees, and wasps, for example, all develop by parthenogenesis. These males are called drones. Only the females are produced by sexual reproduction. Most invertebrates capable of parthenogenesis are also capable of sexual reproduction. Parthenogenesis can be artificially caused in many animals—vertebrates and invertebrates—by treating the unfertilized egg with special chemicals. *See also* ASEXUAL REPRODUCTION; INVERTEBRATE; REPRODUCTION.   A.J.C./C.R.N.

PARTICLE PHYSICS

All matter is made up of tiny particles called atoms. During most of the last century, scientists though that atoms were the smallest particles of matter. They imagined atoms to be very hard, round balls. They thought that atoms had no structure. It is now known that atoms are themselves made up of even smaller particles. These particles are called protons, neutrons, and electrons. (*See* ELECTRON; NEUTRON; PROTON.) They are known as subatomic, or elementary, particles. Usually, they are just called particles. Since these three particles were discovered, many more have been found. The study of these particles is a branch of physics called particle physics (pärt′ i kəl fiz′ iks).

Early discoveries The first subatomic particle to be discovered was the electron. Physicists soon realized that the electron was smaller than an atom. Then they discovered that atoms contain electrons. This meant that the atom had to have some sort of structure. They were no longer thought to be the smallest particles that could exist. In 1911, a New Zealand physicist called Lord Rutherford suggested how to investigate the structure of the atom. (*See* RUTHERFORD, LORD ERNEST.)

He found that atoms contain a very small core called a nucleus. (See NUCLEUS.) He found that almost all of the mass of an atom was contained in its nucleus. The nucleus is surrounded by a number of electrons. The nucleus and the electrons together make up the atom.

Rutherford's theory also explained that the nucleus of a hydrogen atom contained just one particle. This particle is called the proton. It was the second subatomic particle to be discovered. It has 1,860 times the mass that an electron has. The electron and the proton both have electric charges. They have opposite charges that balance each other. The electron has a negative charge. The proton has a positive charge.

The nuclei of all the atoms seem to contain a definite number of protons. This is because their masses are roughly a simple multiple of the mass of a proton. For example, the nucleus of an oxygen atom is just about 16 times as heavy as a proton. Scientists thought that all nuclei contained only protons. They thought the oxygen nucleus would contain 16 protons. But the oxygen atom has only eight electrons. If it also had 16 protons, it would have an electric charge. Oxygen atoms do not have an electric charge. Therefore, there must be particles in the nucleus besides protons. These other particles are called neutrons. They are slightly heavier than the proton and have no electric charge. An oxygen nucleus contains eight protons and eight neutrons. This gives a total weight equal to about 16 protons. Since there are eight protons to balance eight electrons, the oxygen atom now has no electric charge. All nuclei except the nucleus of the hydrogen atom contain neutrons. The neutron was discovered in 1932 by an English physicist, James Chadwick.

The strong nuclear force Physicists then knew that the nucleus contains protons and neutrons. But there was another problem to overcome. Two bodies with a positive charge

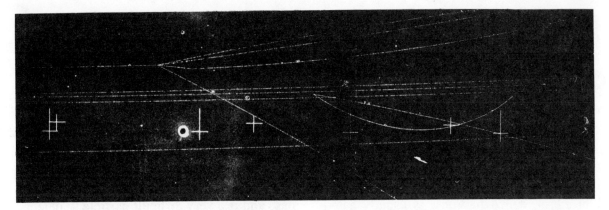

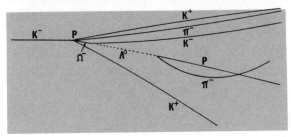

Particles of atomic nuclei which have electric charges leave visible tracks in a bubble chamber. Particle tracks (above) produced by the breakup of a proton particle when hit by a meson are shown. In the key (left), the meson (K^-) hits the proton (P), producing an omega particle (Ω^-), two more mesons (K^+), and a negative pion (Π^-). The omega particle decays to another meson (K^-) and a hyperon (Λ°). The hyperon, having no charge, leaves no track (dotted line). It decays into another proton (P) and negative pion (Π^-).

repel, or push each other away. Therefore, the protons in the nucleus should repel each other since they all have a positive charge. The nucleus should fly apart. In fact, the nucleus is very stable. Physicists realized that there must be a very strong force holding the nucleus together. This force must be strong enough to overcome the repulsion between the protons. It is called the strong nuclear force, or the strong interaction. It is hundreds of times stronger than the electric force. It only works over very short distances, about equal to the width of the nucleus. This is about 10^{-13} cm. (10^{-13} is one divided by ten thirteen times. In the same way, 10^{-6} is one divided by ten six times; this is one millionth.) The strong nuclear force is caused by small particles called pi-mesons, or pions. They are believed to be swapped (given back and forth) between the particles in the nucleus. This swapping of pions creates a very strong force between the particles. Pions were first discovered in 1947 by the British physicist Cecil Powell. He discovered them in cosmic rays. Cosmic rays are streams of subatomic particles. They come from outer space and bombard the earth. (See COSMIC RAY.)

Properties of particles Since 1947 about 300 different particles have been discovered. One way of discovering new particles is by examining cosmic rays. Another important method is to use a large machine called a particle accelerator. (*See* ACCELERATOR, PARTICLE.) In a particle accelerator, streams of particles are made to travel very fast. Then the particles are made to collide with each other. When two particles collide, they sometimes break up. In this way, completely new particles can be made.

All subatomic particles have an antiparticle. These antiparticles have the same mass but the opposite charge. For example, the antiparticle of the electron has a positive charge. It is called the positron. When a particle collides with its antiparticle, the two destroy each other completely, giving off a gamma ray. (*See* ANTIMATTER; GAMMA RAY.)

Subatomic particles have a number of different quantities associated with them. They all have a rest mass. This is the mass of the particle when it is still. When it is moving very fast, its mass increases. (*See* RELATIVITY.) Many particles have an electric charge. This charge can be either positive or negative. The size of the charge is always the same as the size of the charge on the proton and electron. Many particles also have spin. They spin around in the same way a football does when it is thrown. The spin, mass and charge are all fixed for each particle.

Subatomic particles fall into either of two classes, depending on which of the four fundamental forces act on them. (*See* FORCE.) One class, called hadrons, is usually acted upon by the strong nuclear force, and hadrons themselves are divided into two classes: baryons and mesons. Particles of the other class are called leptons. Two forces act between leptons: the electromagnetic and the weak nuclear force, governing radioactive decay.

Baryons Baryons include the proton, neutron, and heavier particles called the lambda, sigma, xi, and omega. These last four particles are all named after Greek letters. The proton is stable and does not break down into other particles. Particles that do break down are said to decay. The neutron is stable when it is inside the nucleus. Outside the nucleus, in about 12 minutes it decays into a proton, an electron, and an antineutrino. The antineutrino is the antiparticle of the neutrino. The other baryons have very short lives, usually less than 10^{-10} second. They decay into other baryons, usually a proton or a neutron. They also give off mesons, leptons, and gamma rays when they decay.

Mesons Mesons include the pions and the kaons. They are all lighter than the baryons and are unstable. They have no spin. There are three pions: a positively charged pion, a negatively charged pion, and a neutral pion. The positive pion is the antiparticle of the negative pion. The neutral pion is its own antiparticle. The positive and negative pions have a lifetime of about 10^{-8} seconds. The neutral pion lasts for only about 10^{-16} seconds. There are four different kaons. A positive kaon has an antiparticle, the negative kaon. There are also two neutral kaons. The mesons decay into a number of different particles. Usually they give off other mesons, leptons, and gamma rays.

Leptons Leptons include the electron, the muon, and the neutrino. They are all very light particles. Both the electron and the neutrino are stable. The neutrino has almost no mass and is a very difficult particle to detect. It can pass through the earth and not collide with a single atom. It was discovered in 1956. The muon is an unstable particle. It decays in about 10^{-6} seconds to an electron, a positron, a neutrino, and an antineutrino. The muon has an electric charge. It was discovered in cosmic rays in 1937.

The subatomic particles can be grouped together in various ways. For example, the proton and the neutron are very similar particles. They form a group of two. The pions form a group of three. Larger groups of particles can be formed in the same way. The particles in these groups can be set in a pattern. Sometimes there is a particle missing in the pattern. There is a gap where there should be a particle. Physicists have searched for this missing particle and have sometimes found it. This was how the omega particle was discovered. Some physicists believe that these groups of particles can be explained. They think that all particles except the leptons are made up of other particles called quarks. (*See* QUARK.) Only twelve different quarks are needed—six quarks and six antiquarks. Then each particle would be made up of different combinations of quarks.   M.E./J.T.

PASCAL, BLAISE (1623–1662) Blaise Pascal (pas′ kal′) was a brilliant French scientist, mathematician, philosopher, and theologian. He did original work in many different fields. He studied atmospheric pressure and made an important discovery in hydrostatics. His discovery is now known as Pascal's law. It states that the pressure at any point in a fluid is the same in any direction. He also studied the mathematical theory of probability. (*See* PROBABILITY.) One of his discoveries in probability is called Pascal's triangle. (*See* PASCAL'S TRIANGLE.) M.E./D.G.F.

Blaise Pascal

PASCAL'S TRIANGLE (pas′ kalz′ trī′ ang′ gəl) Pascal's triangle is an arrangement of numbers shaped like a triangle. It was invented by a Frenchman, Blaise Pascal, in the 17th century. (See PASCAL, BLAISE.) The triangle consists of rows of numbers. The top row has two numbers, 1 and 1. Then each row starts and ends in 1. Two numbers next to each other in a row are added together. The number formed is placed in the row beneath the two numbers and halfway between them.

For example, the fourth row is 1 3 3 1. The first number in the row beneath is 1. The second number is given by 1+3. This number

is 4. The third number is given by 3+3 and is 6. In the same way, the fourth number is 4 and the last is 1. Therefore this row is 1 4 6 4 1.

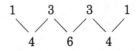

The number of rows in Pascal's triangle can be as many as you like.

Pascal's triangle can be used in a number of different situations. For example, it can be used when you are throwing a number of coins. It tells the likelihood, or probability, of different combinations of heads and tails turning up. Suppose that you have three coins. If they are thrown, there are four possible outcomes. You can have three heads, two heads and one tail, one head and two tails, or three tails. As there are four possibilities, you need the row in Pascal's triangle that has four numbers. This is the row 1 3 3 1. These numbers tell you the probability of each combination occurring. 1, 3, 3, and 1 add up to 8. Therefore there is 1 chance in 8 of throwing three heads, 3 chances in 8 of throwing two heads, 3 chances in 8 for one head, and 1 in 8 for no heads. The chances are the same for throwing three, two, one, or no tails in three coins. *See also* PROBABILITY. M.E./S.P.A.

PASSIONFLOWER (pash′ən flau̇r′) The passionflower is any of about 500 species of dicotyledonous flowering plants belonging to genus *Passiflora*. Most are tendril-bearing climbing plants that live in the tropics. (*See* CLIMBING PLANT.) The flowers grow in the axils and have an unusual and beautiful appearance. They vary in size from 1 to 15 cm [0.4 to 6 in] in diameter. There are five petals and five sepals, all of which are similar in color. Inside the petals is one or more rings of brightly colored, threadlike filaments. In the center of the flower is a reproductive stalk called a gynophore. About half way up the gynophore is a ring of five stamens. Above

A passionflower (facing left) is pictured.

this ring is the ovary with three styles. Each style ends in a large, lobed stigma, giving it the appearance of a large nail or spike. The flower produces an edible fruit—the passionfruit—which may be squeezed for its juice and mixed in fruit punch. *See also* FLOWER. A.J.C./M.H.S.

PASTEUR, LOUIS (1822-1895) Louis Pasteur (päs′ tər′) was a French biologist and chemist. He made many important discoveries concerning bacteria. (*See* BACTERIA.) Pasteur discovered that yeast causes grape juice to ferment into wine. He also discovered that a similar process causes milk to go sour, butter to turn rancid, and wine to turn into vinegar. He developed a process called pasteurization. In pasteurization, food is preserved by heating it to kill its microorganisms. (*See* PASTEURIZATION.) He also developed a vaccine for rabies. He used it to save the life of a child who had been bitten by a rabid dog. In 1888 he founded the Pasteur Institute, which is a center for medical research. The Institute is still in existence.

M.E./D.G.F.

Louis Pasteur

PASTEURIZATION (pas′ chə rə zā′ shən) Pasteurization is a method of preserving food by heating it to kill most of the bacteria or germs in it. The food is then stored in cool conditions. Pasteurization is named for its inventor, Louis Pasteur, a French chemist. It is most commonly used for milk, but may also be used for cheese, beer, and other foods.

The process consists of heating milk to at least 63°C [145°F] for not less than 30 minutes. Then the milk is quickly chilled to 10°C [50°F] or less. This kills most of the bacteria in the milk and allows it to stay fresh for several days. The process does not affect the taste of the milk. Modern dairies use a faster method in which the milk is heated to at least 72°C [161°F] for 15 seconds, then cooled. *See also* MILK; PASTEUR, LOUIS. W.R.P./C.R.N.

PATELLA (pə tel′ ə) The patella, or kneecap, is a small, flat, triangular piece of bone located on the front of the knee. It protects the knee joint. The patella is not directly connected to any other bone. It is held in place by muscle attachments. *See also* ANATOMY.

W.R.P./J.J.F.

PATHOLOGY (pə thäl′ ə jē) Pathology is the study of disease, or of any condition that limits personal health. Pathologists used advanced scientific methods, such as electron microscopy, to help them recognize the changes caused by disease in the tissues and organs of the body. They try to explain why a diseased body acts differently from a healthy body.

Tests by pathologists help physicians diagnose a disease and the extent of its attack. These tests may include the examination of the blood, urine, and tissues. The use of laboratory tests to diagnose disease is called clinical pathology. Pathologists also study diseased parts removed by surgery. For example, persons suspected of having cancer sometimes have the diseased part removed by surgery. It is then analyzed by a pathologist. If the removed part is malignant, or cancerous, further surgery or special treatment may be necessary. Pathologists also examine corpses to determine the exact cause of death. This examination is called an autopsy.

Comparative pathology is a branch of pathology that compares human diseases with animal diseases. Plant pathology is the study of the diseases of plants. *See also* DISEASE; FORENSIC SCIENCE.   W.R.P./J.J.F.

PAULI, WOLFGANG (1900–1958) Wolfgang Pauli (paù' lē) was an Austrian physicist. He was born in Vienna and studied in Munich, Germany. Later he worked in the United States. He made very important discoveries about the atom. He also worked on a branch of physics called quantum theory. (*See* QUANTUM THEORY.) In 1930, he suggested that there exists a particle called the neutrino. (*See* NEUTRINO.) Neutrinos are given off during a radioactive process called beta decay. Pauli studied beta decay and realized that some unknown particle was being given off. He calculated that it should have spin, but no mass. The neutrino was not discovered until about 20 years later. Pauli won the Nobel Prize in Physics in 1945 for his work in quantum theory.   M.E./D.G.F.

PAULING, LINUS (1901–   ) Linus Pauling (pò' ling) is an American chemist. He has studied chemical bonding. When two atoms combine to form a molecule, they are held together by a bond. Atoms combine by means of small particles called electrons. All atoms have electrons.

There are different types of bond. In one type, two atoms share some of their electrons. (*See* BOND, CHEMICAL.) Pauling discovered that these electrons are shared in pairs. A pair of electrons spends part of the time with one atom and part of the time with the other. Pauling then investigated compounds that occur in living tissue, especially proteins. He worked on the structure of their molecules. For this work, he won the 1954 Nobel Prize in Chemistry. He also won the Nobel Peace Prize in 1962. He won it for his efforts in trying to stop nations from building nuclear weapons. He is one of only a few people who have won two Nobel Prizes.   M.E./D.G.F.

PAVLOV, IVAN PETROVICH (1849–1936) Ivan Pavlov (Pa' vlòf) was a Russian physiologist. He is best known for his discovery of the conditioned reflex. (*See* LEARNING AND MEMORY.) Around 1902, Pavlov was experimenting on the digestive juices of a dog. When a dog sees food, it produces saliva. Pavlov rang a bell before the food was given to the dog. After a while, he found that the dog produced saliva when it heard the bell. The dog had learned to associate the bell with food. Pavlov called this a conditioned response. The conditioned response is controlled by a nervous mechanism. Pavlov called this mechanism the conditioned reflex. He believed that the conditioned reflex was the basis of all habits.   M.E./D.G.F.

Linus Pauling

Ivan Pavlov

The peach tree belongs to the rose family. Blossoms (left) and ripe fruit (right) are shown.

PEACH (pēch) The peach (*Prunus persica*) is a tree belonging to the rose family. It is cultivated in temperate areas throughout the world. The tree is usually about 6.5 m [21.5 ft] tall. It has alternate, thin, pointed leaves with toothed margins. The flowers are usually pink and grow in the axils. They have five petals and five sepals. There are three whorls of stamens surrounding a central pistil. (*See* FLOWER.)

The peach fruit has a fuzzy skin. It is round and has a single pitted stone (seed) in the middle. (*See* FRUIT.) The two main varieties of peaches are freestone and clingstone. Freestone peaches have stones which separate easily from the fleshy, edible part of the fruit. The stones of clingstone peaches are more firmly attached.

The peach can be eaten as a fresh fruit, or it may be canned or made into preserves or jelly. It is also made into peach brandy, a liqueur. In the United States, the popularity of the peach is second only to that of the apple. The United States produces more peaches than the rest of the world combined. California leads the country in peach production. *See also* NECTARINE; ROSE FAMILY.

A.J.C./F.W.S.

PEA FAMILY The pea (pē) family includes more than 7,000 species of flowering plants that grow throughout the world. The leaves vary widely, but most are alternate and divided. (*See* LEAF.) The flowers also vary, but most are butterfly-shaped. The seeds are always enclosed in a legume, or pod. (*See* LEGUME.) Most members of the family have small, bacteria-containing nodules on the roots. These bacteria change nitrogen in the air into a form that can be used by the plant as food. (*See* NITROGEN FIXATION.)

The pea plant (*Pisum sativum*) is a vine with pinnately compound leaves and tendrils. (*See* TENDRIL.) It produces seeds—peas—which grow in legumes. The pea is one of the best vegetables in terms of food value. It provides almost as much energy and protein as meat. It is also a good source of vitamins A and C. Peas grown in gardens and used for canning or freezing usually grow on low, bushy vines that are about 1 m [3.3 ft] long. Peas sold as dry peas usually grow on climbing vines that are about 1.5 m [5 ft] long. Other members of the pea family include the alfalfa, bean, clover, laburnum, lentil, licorice, mimosa, peanut, rosewood, soybean, sweet pea, and wisteria.

A.J.C./M.H.S.

PEAFOWL (pē′ faůl′) A peafowl is a bird that belongs to the family Phasianidae. It is more commonly known as the peacock, although peacock is the name for just the male peafowl. The female is called a peahen. There are two species of peafowl. One lives in India. The other lives in Southeast Asia.

The peacock has a beautiful train of feathers which he displays during the breeding season. The feathers of the train are just in front of the bird's true tail feathers. Peafowl make harsh and sometimes startling cries at night. The calls are often mistaken for those of a person in trouble. Peafowl are omnivorous. *See also* OMNIVORE. S.R.G./L.L.S.

PEANUT (pē′ nət) The peanut (*Arachis hypogaea*) is a low-growing, annual plant belonging to the pea family. The plant reaches a height of about 75 cm [30 in] and a width of about 120 cm [48 in]. There are many small flowers which, when pollinated, die within a few hours. (*See* POLLINATION.) The flower is followed by a small stalk called a peg. As the peg grows, the stem begins to bend toward the ground. The peg grows into the ground, sometimes to a depth of 8 cm [3 in]. It then grows an underground legume. (*See* LEGUME.) The legume usually contains two seeds, but it may contain as many as five. It is

these seeds that are called peanuts.

The peanut is almost 50% oil. In most countries, peanuts are cultivated for this oil because it has hundreds of uses. It is a popular cooking oil, a lubricant, a base for soap, and a part of some explosives. Once the oil has been removed, the pulpy remains can be used as a high-protein feed for livestock. Peanuts have more protein, minerals, and vitamins than meat. They provide more calories than sugar. Most of the peanuts grown in the United States are processed into peanut butter. They can also be roasted and eaten, or cooked into many foods and desserts. *See also* CARVER, GEORGE WASHINGTON; PEA FAMILY. A.J.C./F.W.S.

These harvested peanuts will be shipped all over the country for consumer consumption.